PAIN

PAIN

ITS MODES AND FUNCTIONS

by

F. J. J. BUYTENDIJK

Translated by
EDA O'SHIEL

THE UNIVERSITY OF CHICAGO PRESS

Published 1943 in The Netherlands as *Over de Pijn*
by Het Spectrum N.V., Utrecht

Library of Congress Catalog Card Number: 62-9737

THE UNIVERSITY OF CHICAGO PRESS, CHICAGO 37
Published in England by HUTCHINSON & CO., LTD., LONDON, W. 1

To Professor A. Michotte van den Berck
in token of friendship

Preface

*'Nature has perfections to show that she is
God's image and she has imperfections to
show that she is only an image.'* PASCAL

The tendency to split up scientific fields into increasingly smaller
units finds its justification in the fact that a limited choice of
problems and methods facilitates more exact research. In the
natural sciences, and in medicine in particular, the isolation of
specialized fields has resulted in pain being assigned to physiology
and psychology. Each of these disciplines studies pain from a
particular theoretical position. The monographs themselves are
carefully sealed off from one another; a general unifying framework is lacking. In the biological sciences too, where there is still
so much to be done, medicine benefits from this tendency. It
takes the material derived from analytical speculation and applies
it in medical practice.

On the other hand there are two reasons which argue against
the division of science into separate departments, which all serve
to advance human knowledge of man as a whole. First, medicine
serves science and forces it again and again to return to the
original unity of nature, in order to rediscover the deeper significance of independent observations and experiments, the true
nature of facts which are identified, and to determine the principles underlying a comprehensive approach. Secondly, medicine,
that is, practical medicine, requires the maintenance of a certain
niveau with regard to the attitude to man. The only way to
achieve this is to grasp the personal significance of existence in
sickness and health alike. For this is the orbit of both nature and
culture.

7

An examination of the theory of practical pain, the results of which constitute this book, goes beyond the boundaries of technical study for these two reasons. It is a problem which has been treated with a certain awe and emotion by people of all ages. In the forum of the different sciences methodological limitations in the study of pain have become apparent, as well as the need for a synthesis of the issues. This is only possible if we turn anew to the functional and genetic phenomena of life: if we come face to face with man. For man is a creature, who, despite all moral and religious ties, remains physically and psychologically vulnerable in his existential loneliness and desire for society.

Contents

I

Pain and Its Problems

(i) PAIN IN MODERN SOCIETY

'The evils of this world are always more apparent than the blessings.' BOSSUET[1]

IN THE course of daily life, alternating between work and play, sorrow and joy, we rarely express the nature and significance of human existence in abstract or conceptual form. This does not mean that the problems involved are without reality or effect. For basically life is determined according to man's own opinion of himself and his neighbour and of life in its various expressions, not less in what is personal and intimate (and therefore not communicable) than in public manifestations of the life of the community, such as social institutions and governmental machinery. This opinion of oneself is really derived from a long tradition, yet in each age it assumes another aspect.

The greater the unrest in a given period in history, the more pressing is man's need to come to terms with vital questions. Any break with tradition forces us to recast our image of the nature, the origin, and the aim of human destiny, revealing the underlying principles of what we believe ourselves and our neighbours to be. Should these principles become sufficiently differentiated and their relationship to our outlook on society apparent, then they acquire a determining influence on society. They penetrate even the simplest acts of everyday life, both consciously and unconsciously, and shape them after their own fashion. Then the question as to what is the nature and significance of suffering in general and physical pain in particular receives a clear and valid answer. Our whole spiritual outlook and our conduct of life become subject to its guiding principle.

Except in the sphere of religious life, it is difficult to find the conditions necessary to arouse awareness of the problems of suffering in all levels of society and to convince people of the grave importance of meeting such problems. We can see this if we reflect on the nature of these conditions and our reflections are supported by history, especially that of 'the modern era'.

However difficult it may be to recognize the inner motivating forces of contemporary society and to assess these correctly and fairly, we can establish at least one fact. The climate in which the majority of the cultural population of Europe breathes and acts is no longer provided by religion: here the contrast with past centuries is marked. There is no longer a sense of community where each has his place in a single spiritual reality. This fact helps us to understand why men's minds and emotions are no longer preoccupied with the problem of the nature and purpose of pain: the answer is no longer valid for all. A question is worth asking only if it is possible to obtain a valid answer. Since the individual at all times has an insufficient command of personal experience, book knowledge, and powers of creative thought, he has little choice open to him, other than to avoid many vital problems, since his failure to find a solution to them undermines his whole personality.

Man and man's experiences remain essentially unchanged. Modern man, therefore, despite the solitude of his individual existence, and his lack of support from tradition or religion, is forced by his nature and by the character of his experience to inquire into the ground of anything which concerns him *personally*, beyond the immediate occasion itself. There are two reasons for this. In the first place, the cares of daily life, the power of secret impulses, the dangers which threaten both in nature and civilization, and the unappeased desire for material and spiritual goods, all bring man into contact with *reality*. This reality forces itself on him concretely, as the incomprehensible *being* of objects, in that they are of such a nature, and not another. Yet, as experience teaches, this is not incoherent and meaningless, although we feel this rather than understand it. We become fearfully aware of reality in and around us in the form of contact with the distant origin of things, which itself appears as an invisible power. And from our fear a desire to know is born, although we are unable to formulate our question. Even in everyday life, the idea—with which modern man is apparently familiar—of a cosmos which cannot be grasped in concepts of time or space, the notion of man as the outcome of evolution, have been so permeated with emotional elements that they are transformed in human consciousness and regarded in terms of 'fate' and 'chance'.

In the second place, most things which concern the individual, which limit his freedom or which prevent the fulfilment of his wishes or the satisfaction of his desires, are the result of some specific *act* performed by himself or others. This fact too harbours an intrinsic problem as to the ultimate cause; and one which becomes all the more pressing according as it is recognized that freedom and reason are distinctive signs of human nature. The purpose of history, right and wrong, guilt, ignorance, and indolence, all become open to question and compel us to look beyond concrete experiences to remote relationships of ideas.

The inclination and the ability to think independently are the exception rather than the rule. Yet no individual—and this has nothing to do with education or material possessions—can remain unaware of the tension between the fearful notion of fate and the idea of the purpose of history, of himself and the community to which he belongs.

No one with the faintest trace of a philosophy of life can overlook the problem of suffering. Modern scepticism therefore habitually limits itself to what is practical and immediate whenever it is faced with religious or philosophical problems. But the hidden forces of fear and spiritual impoverishment turn such scepticism into a blindness to depth; this reveals itself in the very palpability of things, moods, and passions. Thus a man sacrifices his sense of nature and culture, which above the silence of the one and the noise of the other proclaim the common origin of both. He becomes a prey to loneliness, which he seeks to drown by non-stop activity in the pursuit of material happiness.

Falsification of history and romanticism would convince us that previous generations were less concerned with their own affairs, that they reflected more deeply, were more sensitive and less given to doubt than we. Yet it *is* true that at no time in the past has such a powerful apparatus of instruction and public enlightenment contributed more to destroy reflection than is the case today; so much so that the existence of evil and suffering are no more than registered by our minds. Positive knowledge was never in higher esteem than today. This is the result of differentiation in culture, which creates a technique to bridge increasing distances in time and space. This will soon know no bounds. Man's nature compels him to brood on the purpose of suffering, yet the character of technical civilization inclines him towards scepticism and practical considerations; modern man therefore devotes as little thought to the problem of physical pain as he does to any of the basic phenomena of his existence.

But the *reality* remains unchanged, the reality of suffering and evil. Bossuet realized this long ago. We might therefore expect that the painfulness of pain, the corroding bitterness of all forms of suffering, should be experienced in just the same manner as in times past, that pity should be as profound as in past centuries. But only what forces itself on us as a given *irreducible* fact has the character of reality; if the 'evils of this world' are not experienced as an essential force in human nature they are no longer 'more apparent than the blessings' to human consciousness. A change in the emotional sphere results from this. We can only grasp it when we have a clear knowledge of the connexions between the sensation of pain and our personal attitude to it. For the time being let us establish the fact that pain is a purely individual affair which has nothing to do with metaphysical reality and which is experienced more acutely than anything else; that it does not possess the pathos which results from an awareness of the common bond uniting us with our neighbour and ultimately with the whole human race, whose heavy burden of pain rests in part on our own shoulders.

Modern man regards pain merely as an unpleasant fact, which, like every other evil, he must do his best to get rid of. To do this, it is generally held, there is no need for any reflection on the phenomenon itself. In mental suffering, however, this is indeed very necessary. It is so obviously the result of human relationships, of law and custom, hate and love, social circumstances, education, the community of the family and of one's work, that we are forced to take stock and reflect; this, in its turn, contributes to soothing the suffering and to becoming resigned to what is unavoidable. Suffering caused by sickness and death still stands today characterized by the single idea: the frailty of all that is human.

Pain, irritation *par excellence*, forces us to ask: what is to be done? Medicine, the competent authority for discovering the remedy, has been largely successful, and has made a considerable contribution to the change in the general attitude to pain. Fear of sickness and death is really fear of suffering. Yet the painlessness of modern surgery and the hope of speedy medical aid in case of accident have not had the expected effect of ridding us of the fear of pain nor increased our enjoyment of life.[2]

Someone who has been in an area which is all but cut off from medical assistance knows that resignation, courage, and trust give greater joy than the knowledge that the doctor can be called at any time. Of course this knowledge answers a real need. However, it also causes new fears and above all aggravation when there is a slip in the perfect functioning of the apparatus which medicine and all concerned with it has become. Modern man is irritated by things which older generations accepted with equanimity. He is irritated by old age, long illness, and even by death; above all he is irritated by pain. Pain simply must not occur. Modern society demands that all possible means be used to combat and prevent pain, everywhere and for everybody: in the workshop, at sea, in town and village alike. Advances in diagnosis and therapy are expected to produce more and more such methods, as every doctor, surgeon, obstetrician, and dentist knows to his cost. The consequence is an immoderate state of algophobia (fear of pain) which is itself an evil and sets a seal of timidity on the whole of human life.

Pity felt for suffering is the impulse of medical thought and action, but such a noble motive remains in force only as long as it continues to be inspired by clear insight into the nature of man and the purpose of his suffering. If the association is lost, it becomes a mere technique following its own set rules. If the fight against pain becomes autonomous, it is no longer in the service of mankind and the ethical values of the human order. It follows in the wake of human civilization and aims to approximate its cultural values, a bourgeois form of existence concerned to assure its physical welfare by avoiding all irritations. Part of the same tendency is the determination to combat pain in a radical manner.

Moral judgments relating to a way of life are always open to question. On the one hand there is the opinion that the practical, extremely limited bourgeois outlook on life is synonymous with spiritual impoverishment and a lowering of mental activity, and that the interests of the bourgeois are predominantly concerned with material things. Opposed to this is the opinion that security in a sheltered modest existence is the precondition of a universally valid and therefore ethical order. Whether this is true or not, the bourgeois attitude has certainly overlooked the actual *problem* of pain and the nature and purpose of bodily suffering. It has therefore obscured the delicate relationships between pain and illness, pain and personal existence, in the pattern of human destiny. The image which the bourgeois has of himself lacks any

16

sensitivity. Of course he knows that he may feel pain, but he is not constantly aware of his vulnerability. And so he sacrifices one of the distinct features of human existence.

The progress of medicine in this field enjoys a just reputation: innumerable people are spared great suffering and their subjective well-being is restored. The capacity for work is restored, the sick-bed is more bearable, and even the hour of death is made less fearful. However widespread and justified this reputation, and however proud medicine may rightly be of its achievements, the result has been to transfer the problems occupying mind and the emotions from the metaphysical to the moral sphere, and from the sphere of religion to that of pure fact: what is the purpose of pain? If a man today suffers violent and constant pain, the blame is laid on technical deficiencies, lack of foresight, or the tardiness of medical aid.

However, the desire to avoid pain is quite in keeping with modern religious consciousness. Man has acquired his powers over nature by just means. Even a religious person regards the means of combating pain and illness as a gift of the same order as the benefits of civilization and not *necessarily* harmful to the soul. Although he may acknowledge pain as having more than a mere educative value, in that it strengthens and elevates the character and stimulates reflection, his attitude is quite compatible with the desire to prevent pain. Christian philosophy of life and rules of conduct which carry the weight of centuries of tradition see no contradiction between insight into the extraordinary importance of suffering fulfilling the purpose of human life and perfect trust in medicine and hygiene and their means of preventing pain.

Christian thought and feeling have a special regard for man's natural inclination to avoid suffering: happiness and peace on earth constitute the proper condition and martyrdom is traditionally regarded as divinely enjoined only when it is unavoidable. Such a mature and profound acknowledgment rescues Christian life in the modern technical and pragmatic age from insensitivity with regard to the problem of pain, although it rarely seeks to solve it theoretically.

Many a sick person has no need of words to prove that he has found the true answer to the true question since the existential purpose of pain has been fulfilled by his serene composure and patience in union with Christ, the 'Man of Sorrows'. Then the heart understands something of the saint's joy in suffering, far removed indeed from the spirit of the 'modern world'. Man enters a forgotten world, where the cry of pain has not yet been drowned by the cry to get rid of pain. To modern consciousness the words of a poet such as Francis Jammes might appear incomprehensible, algophile: 'I have nought but my pain and I want no more than it. My pain has been faithful to me in the past and remains faithful to me now.' These words are a testimony like that of St Bernard when he added to the psalm: 'In suffering I am with Him,' 'Lord send me constant suffering that You may always be with me.'[3]

To ask is to stop and look up: the bonds of ceaseless activity are burst and with them the link with transitory things. The serenity of wonder is born within us, the question gives us new perspective. Since the days of Socrates it has been known that the magic of a question depends on its form and on the moment of its being asked. This is true of the problem of pain. Despite practical and pragmatic approaches, despite positivism and rationalism, technical activity and the decline of religious consciousness, it is not always possible, even in modern society, to ignore the significance of pain.

But it is not easy to pose the question in the proper way; an answer is of little help unless there has been a correct formulation of the problem; the sense of wonder is lost. This was shown, for example, in a study of the views of sixth-form pupils by the Saxon Ministry for Education in the year 1934 to select candidates for the University.[4] The question, to be answered in writing, was carefully considered beforehand: Supposing a remedy were to be discovered which prevented anyone who used it from suffering pain, what would the result be? A number of sixth-formers declared that it would be a most welcome remedy, some of them for the strangest reasons: 'the doctors would have less to do', 'they would become more or less superfluous', and 'would be only needed to mend broken limbs', 'the hospitals would become empty'. One even asserted: 'one would get no more pains in one's stomach from eating too much, no headaches from too much thinking, it would be a marvellous invention'.

A few replies gave a momentary glimpse into the true relationship between pain and personal life, for example: 'Men would become even worse than they are already.' 'They could indulge themselves without any unpleasant consequences.' 'They would be indifferent to salvation.' 'At all events it would result in onesidedness and uniformity and consequently human indifference.'

The results of this inquiry need no further comment: they speak for themselves. They show that a vague notion of pain as having a certain purpose and corrective value can be aroused in young people's consciousness. The last answer is the only one which suggests an intimation of the link between pain and the purpose of human life.

The superficiality and primitive formulation of the replies are not, in fact, astonishing. It cannot merely be attributed to the age of those questioned. The replies of undergraduate or even graduate students at a University would presumably differ little. Education is overweighted with booklearning and specialization of scientific training leaves no time for philosophy. The problems of anthropology lie outside the perspective of most 'intellectuals'. Such limitation of one's mental horizons is in keeping with the attitude to pain in modern society; the problem of pain is limited to the question of how to combat it. There are nevertheless indications that the *experience* of pain itself compels us to pose another question and it is this which we would like to examine more closely.

(ii) PERSONAL EXPERIENCE OF PAIN

*'Suffering passes but the fact of having
suffered never passes.'* LÉON BLOY[5]

In personal life there often survives some effective force which has
been lost to the cultural heritage of mankind as a whole. We
have seen that society in our own time has little sense of the
nature and true purpose of pain. The cause of this was seen to lie
partly in the decay of religious life and the consequent decline
of interest in philosophy. We have also spoken of the destructive influence of scepticism on creative thought and how
this is related to the preference for technical and practical
things.

Despite all this, however, language has preserved something
of the original association between the phenomenon of pain and
its metaphysical aspect. The word 'pain' is derived from the Latin
'poena' and originally meant 'punishment'.[6] *'Le mal'* is *'malum'*,
evil, and both concepts are embraced in an aspect of the Christian
doctrine of suffering, in so far as it teaches that God's reply to
'malum quod est culpa' declares *'malum quod est poena'*.[7] The
fact that the fluid medium of language is still able to retain some
appreciation of the connexion between physical pain and human
existence is tacit proof that the problem of pain is in no way the
late fruit of knowledge of nature nor yet the product of subtle
distinctions in philosophical speculation. We are therefore justified in assuming that the phenomenon of pain as an experience
forces man to reflect in the same manner as death forces him to
do. We must examine this assumption more closely and must
therefore begin with an examination of the affective life of man—
his feelings and emotions.

Pleasurable feelings are experienced in an unproblematical
manner. They vary in intensity, level, duration, and effect; and

they appear in more or less close association with sensory impressions, images, judgments, memories, and expectations. Feelings are sometimes divided into two groups, 'vital' and mental, without, of course, overlooking the links between these. Opinions as to the origin of the connexion differ greatly. In general the cause is thought to lie in the vegetative reactions and the sympathetic nervous system. Feelings change in accordance with alterations in the state and flow of the blood, in breathing, and in the activity of the organs of the stomach. Emotional states are affected by such functional changes. Thus a connexion could arise between 'vital' and mental feelings of pleasure through the medium of the physiological processes.

The various feelings are interconnected, quite independently of these physiological processes, by the manner in which they are experienced through integration of the emotions, in the same way as intermodal properties integrate sensory impressions. Just as we may experience a similarity between a bright light and a high note, a heavy scent and heavy music, a smooth surface and a cool drink, in the same way common properties may appear to be shared in the experience of pleasurable emotions.

The very expressions, desire, tension, activity, radiant with happiness, warmth, or satiation try to convey this common quality. Actually these words emphasize the dynamic features uniting a large number of heterogeneous emotions. They are experienced by anyone who is pleased or happy, whether he is stimulated vitally or mentally. An increased intensity is experienced, the stream of life within us seems renewed or strengthened, rigidity gives way to an inner warmth; and we become completely under the sway of this sensation. In feelings of happiness we experience an intensification of well-being, displeasure vanishes, and we sense a release from a former situation which appears to be a negation of the pleasure we are feeling, forming the background against which the present situation is thrown into relief. We need only take a simple example—the first walk in spring, getting up after an illness, quenching a thirst—to realize the significance of both aspects of the experience. In every pleasure something is given to us which supplies a deficit; this is as true in the case of the lower or 'vital' pleasures as it is for the purely intellectual pleasurable sensations and even so-called un-motivated joy. To be filled with pleasure or happiness is a sort of emphasis of life's harmonious oneness, of the association of body and soul, anticipations and reality.

Pleasure is in principle outside contradiction, conflict, con-troversy, tension, or opposition, which are the bases of all problems. In all forms of intense well-being, of physical or mental pleasure, man becomes unaware of his surroundings; he is, so to speak, absorbed by his joy and satiation. The division into subject and object, the experience of an opposite *something* which is also part of the content of consciousness, is alien to pleasure. Pleasure is not thrown into relief against a background of past displeasure as something objective, outside ourselves: it fills, absorbs, and takes possession of us.

Thus the experience of pleasurable sensations *in itself* does not offer the basis for reflection although of course their causal rela-tionships, their link with the present situation, with past and future, and the nature of man and the absolute, can be made the subject of our thoughts. In the actual moment of experience, however, all such considerations vanish, like vain phantasies, un-necessary nuisances. Every question is embarrassing in that we do not know and yet potentially do know: this is completely absent in the all-absorbing moment of joy.

To *dwell* in happiness, to experience happiness *within* our-selves, is foreign to everything which has a problematic character. Even the faintly perceptible flow of numerous small, 'vital', or mental sensations of pleasure which make up our 'normal' health and state of well-being is, as far as experience goes, to quote Scheler, 'metaphysical heedlessness'. Man dwells in a sense of well-being, it is the aim of his endeavours. How quickly we forget suffering and sickness once we have recovered! Leibniz wrote: 'Although health is one of the greatest benefits of the body, it is the one we reflect on least of all and the one we are least familiar with.'[8]

We now turn to the unpleasurable feelings and emotions, considering first the 'vital' feelings, then mental displeasure and its relation to pain, and finally examining the extent to which these emotional states forces us to question and reflect.

Many feelings, each quantitatively different, seem to come from within our bodies, arousing tension and unrest and being experienced as unpleasant. Examples are hunger, thirst, fatigue, oppression, all shades of 'malaise', etc. All these are 'vital' sensations of unpleasure and must be distinguished from unpleasant sensory perceptions such as blinding lights, clashing colours, and similarly distasteful stimuli. In contrast to the latter, the 'vital' sensations of displeasure are not related to an object but to one's own physical state. A person feels that he is tired, hungry, or sick. On the other hand, the irritating or repugnant impression caused by an object or situation is a given property of the external world and does not *in itself* lead to or induce reflection. A person turns away, closes his eyes, reacts, but does nothing about it. Furthermore, such a reaction is the natural means of getting rid of an unpleasant sensation. If this is not successful, the cause does not lie in the feeling itself, nor in its immediate occasion, but in certain complicating factors. The 'vital' feelings of unpleasure, so-called 'vital feelings', cannot be disposed of by a mere involuntary reaction: they require some voluntary act: tiredness demands rest, hunger food, thirst liquid.

The 'vital' feelings of unpleasure adhere to us like a disagreeable mode of existence and are in consequence closely related to pain. Indeed pain is frequently classified under the 'vital' feelings of unpleasure. In fact, however, a considerable difference exists between them; this is of twofold nature. By pain, we mean genuine chronic pain which has to be endured and not the sudden acute smart caused by a blow, sting, or burn. Pain is not merely a temporal disturbance of our state of health, a painful state, but rather, as we shall see, a continued state of affliction limited to a specific part of the body. The other 'vital' feelings cannot be localized in this manner.

The second difference lies in the intellect's response to the emotions. 'Vital' unpleasure in itself, like sensory unpleasure, does not force us to reflect. A given feeling shows quite clearly that it contains its cause in itself and thus urges a person to perform certain actions, e.g. to seek food, rest, etc. These forms of activity can of course be regarded as reactions, in the sense that they are aroused by inner feelings; yet they differ from mechanical reactions to stimuli from without. The latter are not merely more simple, direct, and less conscious: they are also less affected by mental representations, expectations, and other experiences. The difference can be epitomized in the expressions 'reflective movement' or 'instinctive act'.

In summing up we can say that the 'vital' feelings of unpleasure resolve themselves in actions which aim at getting rid of the displeasure. The relationship between feeling and plan of action—that is, its execution—is presented as meaningful, that is, unproblematic to consciousness. As in the case of pleasurable feelings, these feelings in no way urge us to reflect.

A striking difference exists between all forms of mental suffering and physical pain. The difference lies in the questioning attitude which arises out of the feeling itself, not in the intensity, depth, or effect of the suffering. Mental suffering as an experience is interwoven with images and their mutual relationships and has its origin in them. As *psychic* pain, it is in constant union with all psychic processes, feeling, willing, thinking. It produces judgments which help to intensify or diminish it. Consideration of the associated phenomena which arise directly or indirectly from the state of suffering is not the source, but, as it were, the riverbed of the suffering. Mental suffering is surrounded by its own specific problems. But it is not obscure or unclear; it is in itself not even a problem. When we ourselves are caught in the mesh of suffering, as is so often the case, we are so as individuals. Suffering, like joy, can surround and fill us completely. The relationship to thought is analogous in so far as in both cases, joy and suffering, the degree of reflection on the feeling involved affects its quality and intensity. For suffering is particularly sensitive in its reaction to reflection on it.

In contrast to feelings of happiness which, as we have seen, release an inner expansive movement, in which the personality reaches outside itself, oblivious of self, suffering in all its forms is conducive to recollection. It isolates a man from the rest of the world and from all that is without some connexion with suffering. Such limitation of a man's perspective, this constant returning to oneself is not only found in the sphere of emotions but also in that of thought. Mental suffering undoubtedly contains an element of questioning and the questions asked are different from those prompted by physical pain. The difference lies, on the one hand, in the relative transparency of mental suffering; on the other, in the circumstance that physical pain—in contrast to mental—is primarily the experiencing of a senseless conflict *in* one's own personality. We are referring here to bodily pain of some duration, not to momentary pain, which expresses itself perhaps in some violent manner, but rapidly passes and is forgotten.

The ordinary person cannot explain physical pain, and past experience offers no adequate reason. It is understandable that a man should suffer if he loses someone he loves, or as a result of a mistake he has made, or because of unrequited love or an unaccomplished task. Feeling is not so irrational that we find it incomprehensible that a man should be affected painfully in such situations.

No matter how acute the suffering preying on his mind, he can become reconciled to it, because he understands it and because it is a natural part of his circumstances.

A person suffering physical pain questions it in quite another manner. He may be aware of the exact occasion of pain, a wound, or sickness, a swelling—the occasion is anything but a senseless phenomenon, a pointless irritation. But why, he asks, must this wound, this organ, this part of my body give me such acute and continual pain? Why just me? why at this particular moment? why at this particular place? why this abandonment and faintness, this destruction of my freedom, even of thought, sensation, will? why such helplessness? Tormented by pain, the questioning bears the mark of a protest.

Pain is painful in a double sense, since it is also a puzzle tormenting us. Not only our pain, but that of others too, even of animals, leads us, by way of pity, to question. This springs from feeling itself and expresses itself in a formula which is more or less comprehensible without actually being the response of the intellect to the feeling. A person who through his sympathy conjures up the suffering of the whole world, who is sensible to the cry of creation for release from pain, becomes aware in this *cri de cœur* that the problem of pain cannot be waived, any more than can the problem of sickness, death, evil, and sin. In each of these phenomena we sense a sinister disharmony, a conflict with the fundamental reasonableness of life. But in pain alone we actually experience a cleavage in the most natural of all organic unions—that of our personal and physical being.

We are not tormented by some foreign agent, it is not an incident, a word, a thought, or even sickness or death, however we may acknowledge the powers of these: it is our own body. My own hand, my head, hurts me. The organs of the body, the heart, kidneys, stomach, function in a manner which is hidden and unconscious as far as I am concerned: now they refuse to serve, they are in revolt against me: they torment and rob me of my power over myself. This senseless abandonment of the human being to pain has its direct result in a cleavage of the self and the body. Even the animal, far less protected against pain than we, is acquainted with this experience and reacts to it in an elemental manner. No longer in possession of itself, the creature writhes in the mighty talons of pain. The wild cries seem to express its desire to abandon its body to pain. This constitutes a *diffuse flight reaction* evolving round the fixed immovable centre

26

of pain. The creature actually does tend to dissociate itself from its own body when suffering pain: in fact, however, its blind absorption in it prevents it from realizing any such withdrawal.[9]

The natural expressions of pain—screams, groans, moans—all bear witness to the shattering experience of disharmony and the impotence of the creature to prevent the rupture between its self and its physical existence. Joy and suffering fill us, but pain abandons us to utter senselessness; this elemental senselessness of pain drives us not only to protest, but also to seek the active cause outside the boundaries of experience.

It is therefore hardly surprising that the experience of pain should rob us of our 'metaphysical heedlessness' and preoccupy us with the problem of the nature and purpose of this 'evil'. Our unrest may remain unexpressed and unnoticed in the depths of suffering; but the blind man can sense someone approaching, even though he makes no noise; similarly the vague questioning of the sufferer grows in proportion to his feeling of fear and isolation from visible and tangible reality. This feeling springs from the inexplicable nature of pain. The problem of pain in the medium of personal experience becomes one of the possibility of pain's originating within the harmony of life. We experience our own existence as an expression of self-movement, self-preservation, self-realization. Pain, however, teaches us how unfree, transitory, and helpless we really are, and how life is essentially capable of becoming an enemy to itself.

Thus pain is death's shadow and its voice warning us. For experience, death is an end without meaning, incapable of being brought into harmony with life. We only know that there is an ultimate limit imposed on human life and that this can be deduced categorically from the idea that being as a whole must be limited. Pain, however, is a limit *within* our personal life, connected with the organic processes in us and not attached in some way to the periphery. Pain is the most real, and therefore an inevitable and undeniable, evil affecting life *from within*, inhibiting and threatening man. Every human being, even the child and the saint, is a prey to it. The problem of pain, as that of death, belongs to our personal life and can only be solved within its framework.

We die but once and death can come on us suddenly. Pain on the other hand is experienced more frequently and only when we are in a conscious state. 'Suffering passes, but the fact of having suffered never passes.' A man acquainted with the terror of pain is irrevocably changed. Pain itself passes and is quickly forgotten: we cannot recall the sensation. What is then the inner scar which a man carries about with him as the secret mark of a wound long healed? What is the reason for the change in his behaviour, the modification in his judgment, his new attitude to things, to people, to himself? Only the irreparable loss of his 'metaphysical heedlessness' can explain why the fact of having experienced pain never disappears. We could interpret Léon Bloy's words as a bitter complaint, as an indication of loneliness and endurance, or as an appeal for caution in the utterances of one's heart and mind; but such an interpretation stands in contrast to the banishment from the paradise of unawareness, of undisturbed 'metaphysical heedlessness'.

The problem of pain in the community of today is limited to finding the means of combating it: the same natural naïveté leads the individual to regard it at first in the same way. Should pain continue, a second stage sets in, of silence, dumb groans, a cry without words, not for prevention but for release. This cry comes directly from simple natural life and constitutes the metaphysical reaction to an apparently senseless state of affliction, but which cannot be so, since life proves the significance of every single experience.

In the clear light of the thoughtlessness which characterizes a life free of pain, consciousness is filled with sensory impressions and with patterns woven from them by the mind. In the darkness of his pain, man is alone; he is broken inwardly, isolated within his suffering body, and in this state he discovers something new: existing. He does not forget this discovery: 'the fact of having suffered never passes'. Inherent in the personal problem is a question at once philosophical, anthropological, and ontological. No philosophical system can avoid an exact consideration of the problem of suffering, nor does any religion exist which has failed to teach mankind the significance of suffering, why and in what manner the individual must suffer.

(iii) SCIENCE AND THE PROBLEM OF PAIN

'Suffering is a mystery without parallel in the world of this life.' PRADINES[10]

Between knowledge and life there exists an antithesis, even disharmony, which must grieve anyone who turns to science in his search for an answer to the problem of the nature and purpose of his experience. Science is rarely able to answer the questions life sets it. Men are disappointed and even irritated at this, thereby ignoring the character and value of disciplined reflection and methodical examination, the sole aim of which is to discover the laws governing processes.

The attitude of science to phenomena differs from the reaction of the individual. Common to both is wonder at what is taking place and the conviction of reality underlying appearance, as well as an indestructible and necessary relationship in space and time. Man desires passionately an immediate and unequivocal answer which will indicate what he is to do or to leave undone. It must offer him clear insight into his position and his future in his present lack of security and clarity, the result of unco-ordinated experience.

The science of living things and of psychology, which is closely allied to it, are both expected to give particular insight into the true character and significance of the phenomena accompanying individual life, its evolutions, actions, and reactions. One

of the first experiences of University education is the disappoint-
ment felt when the biological sciences are found to give no
answer to the problems the individual regards as important. This
is particularly true in the case of the student of medicine who
meets the problem in the very midst of life and who wants a
solution in order to have a sound basis for his medical work.
Science does not treat sleep and timelessness, movement and rest,
puberty and old age, feeling and intellect, impulse and will,
normal and healthy, for what they are in themselves and what
they signify for human existence, as 'pure phenomena'.

Even if we turn to the textbooks of general psychology we
find little information, thanks to the predominance of positivism
in this science too. Many experiments have been made and
statistical data assembled, but there is hardly a single attempt
made to explain the nature of the emotional life and its expressions
in speech and gesture or its relationship to value judgments, to
ethical consciousness, to the behaviour and norms of the intellect
and the heart. To assume that all these problems are still too
complicated to solve and do not admit of methodical treatment
or analytic examination is just as erroneous as to imply that
science can offer a positivist fundamental knowledge of elementary processes on the basis of which the whole of human reality
can be explained.

We frequently encounter references to the inadequacy of the
human sciences. Their association with the sciences of inorganic
nature is said to constitute an insuperable methodological barrier.
Accordingly many try to solve problems of human life by avoiding methods designed to establish objectively valid facts. It has
been supposed that a literary or poetical treatment of emotional
life would provide what seems denied to science, that is, an
understanding of experience based on exemplary description and
sensitive expression. In our own time the boundaries of scientific
examination as well as the methods and aims of psychology have
become an object of sharp dispute: the argument threatens to
degenerate into a barren discussion of problems of formal

classification. In the course of such examination, many of the alleged barriers have been violated and many formerly accepted methodological principles abandoned.

New fields are being discovered and exploited in science which are no longer part of the approved territory of a particular subject or even an academic faculty: we have new perspectives in the science of human life with the possibility of a great increase in our knowledge. One principle, however, remains unaltered, namely that insight into the essential structure and meaningful associations of things demands that experience be obtained at a certain distance; in other words, that the false perspectives due to emotion involvement must be excluded. In this manner that freedom from self-interest may be achieved which has ever been and will continue to be the motive force of science.

In the study of organic nature the same distance and perspective are required even in the case of phenomena which are only found in fully developed form in human life or in the intimacy of personal experience. Despite the part played by feeling, sympathy, and re-creation in helping us to experience things which could be experienced in no other way, it is only comprehensive knowledge of the conditions, causes, associations, and results which can give true insight into the significance and particular character of all experiences.

A person who has never known pain will indeed be in no position to reflect on it. On the other hand mere experience and introspection are insufficient to make us realize the function of pain in animal and human life. For this a detailed knowledge of the whole field of philosophy and psychology is necessary: the study of pain is part of both of these in being an objective event and a subjective experience. This implies insight into the relationship of physical being and consciousness, of the individual to his milieu, person and world, health and sickness. Furthermore it entails an extensive acquaintance with the facts and the theories of the hierarchy of the organisms, the peculiar position of man in nature, the significance of sense perceptions, and the position

31

allotted to the expressive movements in the entire activity of man and animal.

The problem of pain is a typical biological and psychological problem which, however, can only be formulated if psychologists get away from the urge to explain everything on mechanistic principles and yet retain exact methods of analysis and experiment. At the same time they must not overlook the great contribution of phenomenological analysis, nor allow zoology to be tied to the assumptions of Darwinism. Then, and then only, will it be possible once more to refer animal behaviour, expressive phenomena, and the function of the sense organs to the *idea* of animal being.

But the distinction between bodily processes and consciousness does not mean that these are wholly separated or opposed. This point is fundamental. For a long time, through Cartesian influence, physiology has been treated autonomously and orientated towards physics and chemisty, and physiologists have sought to maintain a barrier between the study of vital functions and that of psychic phenomena, both in method and in practice. A complete examination of the physiology of the senses was supposed to be one which produced a minutely detailed account of the origin and course of nervous excitations. The real task, that is, the achievement of knowledge of the actual function, is only solved by genesis and the system of the forms of relationship between organism and milieu. These consist in perception, attitude, action, and expression. The sciences of living things must first be extended in this manner before the problem of the nature and significance of pain can be formulated and its solution in part supplied.

It has been wrongly held that science, that is, ordered, positive knowledge of causal laws, must necessarily be associated with autonomous natural philosophy, which aims at understanding being by means of the senses. The methodological approach is quite different in the two cases. The object of study of the biological sciences is living organisms. These are given us in the form of relatively autonomous *Gestalten,* the essence of which can be determined in space and time. Bodily forms and functions find a relationship within this essence in a meaningful manner. Thus the organic is the object of science both as a *Gestalt* and as history: the former a totality which can never be comprehended in its parts alone, the latter an independent series of events, taking place through the medium of the *Gestalt*; here what goes before governs what follows after and yet itself is determined by the latter.

All life sciences—physiology, biology, psychology—must therefore refer their factual knowledge in a meaningful manner to the essence of the individual type, family, tribe, or empire to which each belongs. Meaningful associations constitute the object of every life science. Biology is more than a natural science, in so far as this is defined, on the model of physics, as knowledge of laws and, as far as possible, their mathematical formulation.

'Biology,' according to Weizsäcker, 'does *not* belong to the life sciences and has therefore no right to the quantitative method. Indeed,' he continues, 'it becomes quite incomprehensible if we assume that its task is no different from that of physics and chemistry: it must rather accomplish what they do a second time and under far more difficult circumstances.'[11]

Living activity is historical and formed and is therefore necessarily associated with spatial and temporal *representations.* Biology is therefore 'determined by representations'. Its point of departure is to discover qualities and establish connexions between them. The same aim governs the physiologist's experimental work, although his method is analytical: the facts and knowledge he has gleaned by various means must be merged into a representation of living activity. Sometimes the image can be constructive and mechanical since many processes in the animal organism are partly mechanical—the functions of the blood, the action of the muscles, the heart beat, or the filter function of the kidneys. Side by side with these, there is the model of the whole organism interacting with its milieu. This connexion cannot be comprehended mechanically, because the impressions which release the movement, like the movement itself, are always qualitative and formed. Analysis only shows the means whereby the animal functions operate.

An error must be pointed out in this connexion, namely that of trying to explain human and animal behaviour in terms of the nervous system. Of course the structure and the function of the latter, like all internal and external conditions, are invaluable in throwing light on factors which precondition but do not in any way constitute the real origin of what is taking place at any given moment, and in a specified location. That is not to say that a detailed knowledge of physiological processes and the structure underlying these is not important in helping us to grasp the individual functions and the sensations and feelings they produce. Functions and means of execution are correlated in the living being. Experience teaches that every part is related to the whole of the organism: therefore a study of the processes in each part of a sense organ and the nervous system contributes to solving the problem of pain. Just as our understanding and enjoyment of a musical composition is increased by a knowledge of the various elements of musical technique, similarly morphological analysis increases typological knowledge of an animal species. In exactly the same manner our insight into the significance and quality of human feelings and expressive reactions is extended in accordance with our knowledge of the numerous partial phenomena and their interrelationships; for these have a share in bringing about individual experience and activity. We are reminded of Goethe's words: 'Nothing takes place in living nature which is without connexion with the whole, and though experiences may seem to us to be isolated, when we are taught to regard experience as isolated facts, yet that does not imply that they really are isolated.'

In the interests of the study of the individual and personal functions, it is necessary to bridge the gap between physiology and psychology. However, the detailed method of analytical experimentation must not thereby be underestimated.[12] A knowledge of physiological processes, morphological structures, and phenomena of consciousness obtained by laboratory experiments has an important contribution to make towards solving the various problems raised by the phenomena of pain.

The life sciences have always inquired into the purposefulness of form and function, and in doing so they have been guided by the effectiveness of organs, frequently from the point of view of the principle of economy. In the case of the organism as a whole, they consider the purpose of the constituent parts and their behaviour, vis-à-vis self-preservation and the preservation of the species.

Thus a typical question in biology would be whether pain is or is not *useful*, whether it serves a definite purpose, in the series of regulative processes which make up the integrity of the bodily structure, the work of the organs, and the continued existence of the individual and the species in a particular milieu. Methodologically speaking, the thesis that pain is purposeful places biology in an awkward position. This has two aspects: firstly, in face of the generally accepted principle that biology, like all natural sciences, is exclusively concerned with causal relationships, at any rate, with formal knowledge of the laws whereby phenomena operate. Considerations of purposefulness are then only an 'heuristic' principle, that is, a means of tracing relationships and not a direct contribution to the knowledge of the object itself. Secondly, the basic principle of mechanistic physiology which flourished in the latter half of the last century denies the relevance to biology of sensations and other contents of consciousness which 'accompany' physiological processes.

Thus the question of the potential purposefulness of pain can only refer to the effect of *physical* phenomena which are accompanied by a feeling of pain. It is therefore hardly surprising that even those instances which appear to be characterized by purposefulness (e.g. withdrawal of a foot which has stepped on a nail) prompt us to ask why such purposeful reactions should also be accompanied by pain. To refer, as Richet[13] has done, to the warning character of pain, which teaches men and animals to avoid repeating a painful experience, is to transcend the boundaries of physiology as a science of physical processes.

If, on the other hand, we are to regard pain as part of the field of psychology, we are still bound to explain that all reactions to pain-producing impressions are physical processes. Furthermore, if we limit psychology to the study of processes of consciousness, biological and functional viewpoints recede to the background and with them the whole problem of pain and its role in animal and human life. The degree and quality of pain is more dependent than any other feeling on its accompanying expressive movements and autonomic reactions (not caused by pain). If we take note of this common experience we can convince ourselves that the problem of pain is not exclusively psychological.

Two further obstacles to a scientific treatment of pain must be noted. The first is connected with the experience that pain places our body in opposition to our self-consciousness. Before appreciating such a fundamental quality of pain, it is necessary to set up a theory of 'bodily experience' in general as well as the manner in which the latter is experienced.

This is not primarily concerned with localization of pain and Lotze's theory of 'local signs', or the thesis of the body image (Schilder),[14] or the ontology of bodily existence as such. Impartial scientific treatment with its deliberately limited sphere demands reflection on the unusual relationship between man and animals and their milieu and their own bodies. The terms far and near, 'alien' and 'own' (E. Straus),[15] centric and 'excentric', 'positionality' (H. Plessner),[16] are part of biology. Without these terms it would lose much of its deep insight and breadth of vision with regard to its subject.

Another problem appears to be whether pain is a 'normal' phenomenon or a type of affective response which lies outside the normal boundaries of life. In the latter case pain would be part of pathology, not physiology, and it would be meaningless to inquire into its purposefulness. Its association with sickness, injury, and death would be more relevant. Since the ordinary sense perceptions are the individual's normal means of contact with the outside world, according to this interpretation pain would have no place among the 'normal' sensory functions. Yet a pathological process of any sort, so common in everyday life, cannot be excluded from biology, and the same applies to pain, the reaction to injury, the healing of a wound, and morphological and functional regeneration or adaptation.

The science of living things can only set itself to investigate—and possibly find an answer to—the problem of pain if the organism is really seen as a living being: that is, as alive some-*where* with sensory and motor functions inseparably united. Furthermore these sensory processes are not merely passive excitations: they are determined by the individual's own activity and attitude. In the special case of man they represent 'a meeting between self and the outside world' (v. Weizsäcker);[17] they are not a series of causes and effects, they are motivated 'decisions'. In a word, only biology, which is distinguished in principle from the study of inorganic nature, which possesses its own terminology and explanatory principles, and which at the same time is not separated from psychology, since biologists are concerned with an object within which a subject dwells, biology alone holds the key to the problem of pain.

Both in direct experience and scientific experiment, the individual existence of an animal is characterized by the indissoluble union of physical and psychological phenomena. Each of these retains a relative independence. The contradiction of union and body-mind parallelism must be accepted as an irreducible fact. The psychophysical union is just as incapable of being grasped by the imagination as the interaction of parallelism of body and mind. Neither this circumstance nor the difficulty arising from the problem of being and consciousness can allow philosophical speculation to neglect either of these viewpoints in its concern with a concrete object. And yet this does occur frequently.

37

In the past, emphasis was placed rather on the independence of the physical and psychical, whereas today the tendency is to see the organism exclusively in the light of psychophysical unity. Apart from an endless series of long-winded discussions of 'wholeness', there are many modern studies in neurology, psychiatry, characterology, and typology centring on the unity of human and animal existence. Recent experimental studies of balance and dizziness, such as those by Vogel[18] and Christian,[19] testify to the close bond between sensations, feelings, and movements. Finally there are valuable papers on expressive movements which make us feel that we can almost reach out and grasp the psychophysical unity (Klages).[20] The opposition which exists between the physical and psychical is momentarily forgotten. Plessner,[21] however, in his excellent study of laughing and crying, has proved that these forms of utterance 'on the periphery of human behaviour' can only be explained if we recognize that, despite all apparent unity, the fundamental structure of body and soul is one of polar opposition.

From time immemorial, the doctor, with his disregard for theories in his daily work, is the one who is most deeply aware of the unity, combined with mutual independence, of subject and object. As Weizsäcker has said, he takes his diagnostic bricks wherever he can find them and he unites without further ado the subjective explanations of the patient with the objective symptoms. Because of his modern (positivist) training he will probably give preference to the latter. But he would think it foolish to disregard any subjective explanation, no matter how seemingly insignificant, to help him in a difficult case.

The doctor's thought and his actions are the result of personal contact between himself and his patient, which prevents the true medical aim and ethos from ever being lost sight of. He is neither scholar nor artist nor technician; he is simply a doctor (Krehl).[22] 'His activity has much in common with theirs, but in the final analysis his aim is a totally different one: it embraces far more, since the object of his work is man as man.'

The diagnosis of a doctor does rest, to a certain degree, on a generally accepted scheme of physical processes, the causes of their being interrupted and the means of restoring equilibrium. This knowledge is applied independently of personal factors affecting the sick person. At most the patient's life history, constitution and milieu, which can be gauged by objective examination, have a certain contribution to make. But when the patient calls for help in his *suffering*, then the doctor is no longer concerned with a 'case', but with a sick man, and more is required of him than could be expected from a scholar or technician. The doctor is expected to understand man, in health and in sickness. This is no ordinary understanding: the patient must be brought face to face with himself and his neighbour. He must be brought to ask himself what is the purpose of his life and what are the ethical demands made on him. O. Schwarz[23] in his *Medizinische Anthropologie* has this in mind when he speaks of the problems of medicine as having 'their roots in the philosophy of the mind'. A doctor's contact with suffering human beings brings him time after time face to face with the problem of pain in all its complexity.

A doctor seeks from the natural sciences the basis of his professional treatment. But in addition he needs to have more intimate knowledge of the human personality than the layman has, and his experience provides him with some knowledge of human society. It would be too much to expect the doctor to have a thorough philosophical training, and a bare acquaintance with its tenets and history would be of little avail. But he must reflect a little on man, on human nature as a whole, and on the way the patient's mind works, before he can hope to understand the nature of his suffering. The general decay of philosophy and the divorce of psychology from physiology—though in practice this is often ignored—constitute a serious obstacle to the proper approach to the problem of suffering, that is, pain.

A doctor examining a sick man discovers the secret of the

simultaneous unity and conflict of conscious and unconscious psychical life in its physical manifestations and sees how the conflict can be overcome in the free, rational ethics of the mind.

The nature of the object of medical science is such that it can form the basis of theoretical biology and philosophical anthropology and thus hope to treat the problem of pain scientifically. This is, of course, only true in so far as it takes its object, man himself, in health and sickness, seriously. Three factors force a doctor to concern himself with pain. First, as Hippocrates taught, he is called by God to relieve it; secondly, it provides him with a valuable symptom of disease, and finally, despite the objectivity of his outlook, he is brought into closer contact with pain than anyone else. Of course his reaction may also be one of pity, but his office is not to console but to heal and therefore to know. Emotional ties impair and prejudice his judgment and the appeal for distance and the exclusion of partiality has a special relevance in his case, even though his first concern is with the humanbeing. and then with the disease. A doctor at a bedside sees the image of man in pain in the tense fear of the features, the dilated pupils, the pallor and cold perspiration, the dynamic restlessness of the sufferer, his despairing words and his plea for help. These enable the doctor to recognize the link between pain and vegetative life and with everything that is human and personal. He recognizes this link in qualities of character, in ethical values, in the hidden forces of the unconscious, in the power of the will, and the relationship of man, bound in torment to his own body, to himself and God.

Then the doctor discovers the extent and the depth of pain, and its connexion with physiological, psychological, pathological, and personal events: with animal and human being. Pain compels him to silence. It is not merely a problem, but a mystery —'a mystery without parallel in the world of this life', a senseless element of life. It is a *'malum'* placed in opposition to life, an obstacle and a threat, which throws man aside like some wretched creature who dies a thousand times over again.[24]

In the night of unfathomable senselessness, the doctor at the bedside becomes aware of a mysterious light: that which is eternally unchangeable in man and which contains the meaning hidden in the apparent senselessness of the world.

II

The Physiology of Pain

(i) SKIN PAIN AND THE PAIN SENSE

'Pain is never the quality of an object.'
ACHELIS[25]

THE physiology of pain is concerned with the way a sensation of pain arises, and with the nerve endings, fibres, and other elements of the nervous system involved. It is concerned, furthermore, with the organism's reaction to the painful impression. On the basis of this knowledge, it attempts to form a picture of the function of pain in changing circumstances.

In the course of its development through the various experimental tests and discussions of different experimental methods—to be found in every handbook—physiologists have worked out a number of viewpoints. These have assessed the significance of pain as a phenomenon and its limitations.[26] We do not intend to investigate the analytical studies devoted to the question. The most relevant facts will be considered, as well as their mutual relationships, as an aid to solving the problems associated with pain.

Firstly, let us examine the connexion between skin pain and the sense of pain. The painful impressions which are most commonly incidental in everyday life are caused by stimulation of the skin. The skin is therefore regarded as the normal specific organ of painful sensations. Such sensations would thus constitute one of many kinds of impressions which arise on the skin when it is touched by an object. Besides the senses of touch, pressure, heat, and cold, there would also be a sense of pain. Every skin sense has its own special nerve-end organ, which causes a specific sensation to be aroused by an adequate or inadequate stimulus.

If pain results from the stimulation of a particular sense, the sensation of pain cannot be caused by the stimulation of other nerves or nerve-end organs. At first normal experience seemed to contradict this view. Intensive stimulation of any nerve is painful, as cuts and surgical operations confirm. Even strong light and a loud noise are felt to be painful, as is intense stimulation of the mucous membrane of the nose or of the tongue. But the cause of the painful sensations in all these instances can be shown not to be stimulation of other senses or their nerve fibres, but rather the simultanous stimulation of pain fibres, which are found everywhere in the human body. If the sensory nerves of the eye (other than the optic) are severed there is no longer a painful reaction to strong light. The contraction of the iris in strong light is particularly painful. The pain produced by a very loud noise can be traced to cramp in the inner muscles of the ear, or as a result of pressure on the eardrum. There are numerous pain fibres in the mucous membrane of the nose and tongue which can be stimulated by chemical substances.

Ordinary experience shows that increased pressure, heat, or cold causes sensation to turn into pain. Investigation has demonstrated, however, that a large number of sensitive nerve endings lie close to one another in the skin and that they are affected simultaneously by natural contact with objects or air currents, as well as by touch, heat rays, effects of chemical substances, or electricity. If the stimulus is slight, it may be that only pressure and temperature senses react. If it is increased the pain receptors or nerve endings, which are specifically sensitive, respond also. This transition is commonly experienced: it originates in different degrees of sensitivity and in the position of the various skin organs. Experimental research also proves the existence of *particularly* sensitive points in the skin, besides pressure, heat, and cold points. In some parts of the body one or several of such

43

nerve endings are missing. In the cornea of the eye, for example, there are only pain points.

The distribution of these various pain points over the surface of the body and also their sensitivity to mechanical and other stimuli have been measured exactly. But the net result for our knowledge of their functioning has been small. On the other hand something has been learnt of the different types of skin pain sensations. There is a sharp clear pain, as when a thin fold in the skin is pinched, and a dull pain, which may turn into an ache, if strong pressure is applied on both sides of a broad skin fold. A distinction is made between superficial and deep skin pain, and the sensation following burning, which is quite different again.

The variety of these sensations seemed to indicate the existence of several kinds of pain receptors in the skin. Samples examined under the microscope were seen to contain nerve endings of varying structure. Except for a few types, their function is not known. It is fairly certain that the narrow nerve fibres are pain receptors. These end between and occasionally inside the cells of the outer skin.[27] By gently touching the centre of the cornea, where only thin nerve endings are to be found, it is possible to produce tactile impressions in certain circumstances.[28] According to some investigators it is possible for a very slight mechanical stimulation of a pain nerve ending to produce a sensation of pressure and for a light thermal stimulus to produce a non–painful impression.[29]

Whether we accept this or not, the original concept of skin pain was that of a single sensory quality, mediated by the stimulation of one kind of nerve ending only; a separate pain sense was therefore postulated alongside touch and temperature senses. This has now given way to the opinion that several impressions of pain exist and that the sensory qualities are conditioned by several other factors.

The sharp pain caused by the prick of a needle must be treated separately. This pain is a clear, short-lived, well-localized impression; in many respects it is related to a touch impression.

If intense, '*la sensation de piqûre*' (Piéron) is undoubtedly painful, but it differs from other pain impressions in that it tells us something about a property of the objects, namely their sharpness.

We should therefore speak of painful tactile impressions rather than of a pure sensation of pain. In addition the rapid transmission of the impression of sharpness or prick through the nerves to the central nervous system belongs to the same order as the speedy transmission of the ordinary non-painful touch impressions.

'Genuine' skin pain is quite independent of any impression of sharpness and is a feeling of restless burning or continuous dull penetrating pain, which can have additional qualities according to its location, extent, and duration. This skin pain is called 'genuine' because it shares many of the characteristics of pain in other parts of the body. It can have several degrees of intensity. It is hard to locate and tends to spread beyond the point of stimulation. It is not limited in time; it increases and decreases and alters according to external and internal circumstances. It does not refer us to an object: it is simply an *affect*. This sensation, to be known briefly as *skin pain*, can be examined experimentally. It can be produced by various agents: pressure, heat, intense cold, electric current, chemical substances.

The speed with which pain is conducted in the nerves is most important. It shows that deep, dull, 'genuine' pain is conducted by the narrow nerve fibres at a low speed of about one metre a second. Touch and sharp pain are transmitted at a speed of about 20–40 metres per second.[30] This can be easily demonstrated. If we touch a small point on the surface of some hot object (about 65° Centigrade) with our hand or, even better, our foot, for a brief interval (about half a second), we only feel a short prick at the moment of contact. About a second later this is followed by another sensation which disappears quickly and is slightly painful.[31] The location of the receptors for this 'secondary' pain is still uncertain. Probably they are the narrowest nerve fibres which are found at varying depths in the skin and around the smallest blood vessels, the roots of the hair, etc.

It would seem from various experiments that skin pain is produced by chemical substances which are released by various stimuli and injuries to the cells and which then stimulate the nerve cells.[32] Apart from these and other particular issues not yet fully accounted for, we are forced to admit that studies of skin pain have not proved the existence of an actual pain sense.

There is no such thing as a pain sense as there is a touch or an optical sense. There is a quality in pain sensation which cannot be produced by intensifying other sensory impressions but only by stimulating certain groups of nerve fibres. But this does not prove the existence of a specific *sense* of pain.

A sense organ is the organism's means of communication. Its function causes it to be attuned to a specific, adequate, external stimulus. Therefore the sensation produced by sensory impressions is always related to *things*. In the case of pain this is not so. Skin pain, as we have seen, is produced by various factors and the sensation of pain does not refer to the quality of the irritant. Pradines, whose important work will be considered when we discuss the origin of pain, says: 'Each sense has its own specific stimulus corresponding to some quality in the objects. Pain has only common stimuli: these do not specify any physical quality.'[33] Investigations also show that skin pain varies greatly even when the stimulus remains the same and that it is not closely connected with its external cause.

Skin pain, like all pain, is the experience of a physical state being disturbed in a manner for which the subject is not prepared. The shock causes it to react. 'Pain does not explain anything objectively; its role is merely to make us aware of the evil by means of an instantaneous sensation.' 'Pain is just of the order of passion and reaction' (Pradines).[34]

As early as the mid-nineteenth century E. H. Weber[35] disputed the suggestion that pain belongs to the senses since it does not give us information of any kind. Yet every pain in our body is *localized* and skin pain can be localized fairly exactly. In his excellent *Allgemeine Sinnesphysiologie*, which is far too often overlooked, J. v. Kries[36] notes that 'somatization' of pain sensation is to be regarded as a 'stage before objectivization of pain'. It is possible to experience painful impressions on the skin or elsewhere, say on the mucous membrane of the nose and mouth, as subjective affections, and yet, at the same time, in their relationship with some objective event, experience them as being connected with some objective occurrence. When clothes rub on a sore part of the skin we say they are painful, or we refer to a 'biting' odour or taste.

Skin pain is usually studied as far as possible in isolation. In normal circumstances skin pain is always connected with sensations of touch and temperature. It yields impressions which are apparently sensory yet at the same time remind us of a non-sensory element. It is only in the case of contact with a sharp object that the acute painful impression which results is sensory. However, like the impression of heat, roughness, wetness, etc., it is the result of the co-operation of several skin receptors. An analysis of other objective impressions, for example weight, resistance, position, and movement, shows a single sensory perception is made up of several kinds of sensations. We therefore conclude that skin pain can be an element in a sensory perception but that a skin sense as such does not exist.

(ii) THE CONNEXION BETWEEN SKIN PAIN AND ITCH

'It is impossible to draw a clear distinction between itch and protopathic pain.'
ROTHMANN[37]

Genuine skin pain in the sense already mentioned is usually termed protopathic and is distinguished from epicritic pain. The latter is the well-localized pricking pain, the *'sensation de piqûre'*, which is very closely associated with the touch function of the skin. Rothmann, amongst others, declares that protopathic pain cannot be separated from itch and describes it as an 'unpleasant, burning, diffuse sensation'. v. Frey[38] was the first to expound the theory of itch as a non-intensive burning feeling. We can observe the connexion between skin pain and itch in our own lives. Pain which lasts some time but is never very acute is inclined to give way to an itching sensation. The association of the two forces us to investigate how far slight skin pain is functionally important: has it indeed any significance for the organism as a whole?

Before indicating the results of physiological investigations, let us examine the general functional significance of itch. An animal's (or human being's) contact with the outside world by means of the skin consists firstly in the functional circular process between touch and movement: an example of this would be feeling an object or walking across a soft, hard, or uneven floor. In these cases the impressions (on the fingers and soles) produce motions, and these, in their turn, also release impressions.

Secondly, there is the sudden touch which results either in genuine contact when the animal feels the surface of the object, or in a flight movement when the touch is harmful or 'nociceptive'. Such flight reactions, like withdrawing one's hand, are not the response to pain; they actually precede it. In these cases the swiftly transmitting nerve fibres are probably geared to the 'vital' purposeful reactions. Itch appears between the moment when contact results in sensory impressions releasing movements and these, in their turn, sensations, and the sudden stimulus followed by reflective motions. Itch appears suddenly; it does not cause contact: it *irritates*. Irritation is primarily unrest; it is expressed in movements which must be rhythmic in character. Stimulation of the skin leads to scratching movements which are not at first localized; they occur along the surface of the skin and get rid of the irritation. Itch, like pain, is not a sensory perception. The objective cause of the itch can be comprehended by

48

the mind: it is not contained in the sensation itself. We are concerned here with an irritation which movement gets rid of. The same is true of flight motions, but here pain has no functional share in the process of movement; it only appears after the limb has been withdrawn. Itch has a functional role in the process since it is a *feeling* of irritation which occasions and prolongs the scratching movements until these have caused it to disappear.

Here, too, the connexion between movement and sensation is analogous to that between movement and affect. Actions and feelings do *not* form part of a circular process. The former are occasioned by the latter and cause them to vanish, whereas in the case of a genuine sensori-motor circular process not only do the impressions produce movements but conversely the movements occasion impressions. In pathological cases we do find a similar state of affairs with itch. Scratching movements create itch and this necessitates scratching. The circular process cannot stop itself and the normal reaction to a feeling of itch is no longer sufficient. As we know from experience, the relationship can only be dissolved by an external factor. This can be done by firmly checking the movements or reducing the itch by cooling; or the skin can be irritated to such a degree that the itch gives way to pain (wounding or applying pressure with a nail).

The analogy between the relationship of itch and movement, on the one hand, and that of emotion and emotional action, on the other, needs to be examined more fully. Generally speaking it is the function of emotion to provide or maintain the stimulus to an action (or expression). This is unquestionably the case with emotions such as anger, fear, or gaiety. The *form* of the movement is obviously determined by the sensory impressions of the situation while the *general* character of the movements is laid down by the *feeling* of the motor pattern. This feeling determines the category of the actions, the general scheme of the area, and type of movement. Hunger impels us to seek, anger to be aggressive, fear to flee.

Are then pain and itch analogous in their functions and can they be classed as emotional situations? Sudden injuries to the skin are followed by flight movements and then by pain. Perhaps this feeling increases the tension of the contracting muscles and prevents them from stretching. Vivisectional experiments have revealed a similar phenomenon, the so-called 'after-discharge', caused by a stray irritation in a particular section of the central nervous system. Perhaps something similar takes place in the integral animal and in man. Is pain nothing but the feeling accompanying this irritation? But why should it be painful? We shall have to return to this question again.

The connexion between feeling and movement is more obvious in the case of itch. Burning, restless, irritating secondary pain bears some slight resemblance to an itching feeling and is gradually transformed into it. Not only is this a sort of restlessness, but as a sensation it is also dynamically related to the scratching movement. The emotion of anger, the feeling of 'being about to burst' is related to explosion and aggression, while fear or fainting has a dynamic similiarity to the kind of action it produces. Thus itch, in so far as it is an affect, is also a rhythmic stimulation and a virtual movement, related to the actual motion which it brings about.

K. Wilde discovered various basic forms of rhythmic stimulatory sensations and described them in his article, 'Zur Phänomenologie des Wärmeschmerzes'.[39] He describes types of 'heat sensation': thus a feeling of warmth is felt, followed by a 'shivering sensation' as the intensity of the irritation, which constitutes 'the threshold for this particular type', increases. This is described by experimental subjects as 'a rapid sequence of brief touch sensations at a frequency of 10 or more per second'. The speed slackens briefly till it reaches a constant frequency of 4 to $\frac{1}{2}$ per second, according to the part of the body. At the same time a rhythmical pricking appears ('prick sensations'). Wilde disagrees with v. Frey's theory in asserting that the itching sensation may turn into a feeling of pain after the painful stimulus has exceeded a certain degree of intensity. This question is not essential in our present context.

There are, at all events, several intermediate stages between itching and burning pain; these depend on circumstances—on the degree of awareness, suggestive influences, temperature, and on such factors as expansion and compression of the skin. It is fairly certain that all stimuli resulting in an itch cause chemical changes and subsidiary reactions in the blood vessels of the skin, probably through accumulation of a specific chemical substance —histamine—and that this is dispersed by rubbing and scratching. If this substance is introduced into the skin it can cause itchiness as well as pain. It appears when cells are damaged, as by burning.

Itchiness also disappears if the sensibility to pain is got rid of. In the case of facial pain Sjöqvist was able to effect analgesia but retain the sense of touch by severing the narrow pain transmitting fibres in the spinal cord. It was now no longer possible to reproduce shivering and itching sensations in the operated nostril. Zottermann[40] concurred with this opinion in his electrophysical examination which showed that the nerves transmitting the itch (and tickling) sensation are the same as the fibres transmitting secondary pain (genuine or protopathic pain). Like burning pain, the latter is also related to the sympathicus. In addition it appears that the itching (and tickling) sensations in skin irritation can be checked by stimulating several of the swiftly transmitting fibres (touch and primary pain fibres). This may explain why mechanical stimulation such as rubbing, pressing, or pinching are capable of dissolving or reducing both itch and burning skin pain.

There is still much uncertainty in this branch of physiology and the pathological states associated with it. We do not know why some skin affections itch so acutely and why scratching only makes things worse. We shall see that there is a close connexion between pain and the sympathetic nervous system. Dermatologists are aware of the remarkable relationship between itch and sympathetic innervation.

If it is true that there is no clear demarcation line between protopathic pain and itch, slight skin pain is undoubtedly purposeful. That means that it has a function in the life of vertebrates whose skin can be stimulated by various means, such as by parasites, chemical substances, etc. It causes scratching movements by means of which the itching sensation is dispersed. The nature of acute skin pain is totally different from itch and the reactions to it quite distinctive. In a later chapter we shall consider the biological significance of this latter type of skin pain.

(iii) PAIN AND MOVEMENT

'A theory of pain cannot exist which contents itself with a guiding principle derived from the periphery.'
V. WEIZSÄCKER[41]

There are numerous associations between pain and movement, or, more accurately, between pain and activity in general. Experience proves this in different ways. Pain is caused by movement and tensening of the muscles. Screaming and other expressive movements such as clenching one's teeth or fists, that is, making the muscles tense in any way, helps to relieve pain. Complete rest and relaxation of the muscles have the same effect. There is an almost total lack of systematic studies on the connexion between pain and activity. Piéron[42] did establish that sensitivity to pain is lessened somewhat by making tense the arm and jaw muscles; however, the degree of concentration necessary to measure the pain threshold is so great that it interferes with any other activity. Our knowledge of the association is, therefore, gleaned from isolated facts in clinical experience and from special analysis of direct experience. Although quantitative tests are lacking, this group of facts is important not only for physiology in general, but for the particular problems connected with pain.

Let us first of all investigate how moving or making tense the muscles should cause pain. Continuous work produces tiredness —a feeling which makes itself felt long before exhaustion: the two must be carefully distinguished. The appearance of exhaustion has been carefully analysed in the physiology of work; it is found to be brought about by an insufficient supply of oxygen in the muscles, in consequence of which the content of blood sugar drops. Tiredness is a feeling which appears during and as a result of work, partly as a general inability and partly as a localized effect. Tiredness can also appear without any particularly intensive task having been performed; it can result from standing for a long period, abnormal posture of arm or back, or lying on a hard surface. It is a common feature of illness, in its various states, on its first appearance (temperature), or during convalescence, when a patient gets up for the first time. Some poisons have a similar effect.[43]

Pain, in my opinion, is caused, in the majority of these cases, by the stimulation of the protopathic (deep) pain receptors. Occasionally this is quite obvious. A painful injury to one's foot prevents one from walking far, an ulcer on one's hand or neuralgia brings about a tired sensation in the affected area. Tiredness as a result of standing or abnormal posture is a dull, deep pain in the joints, sinews, ligaments, and muscles.

The painfulness following tiredness causes abnormal tension of the muscles and this increases the feeling of tiredness. The feeling and slightly painful sensation of weariness can also be caused by swelling of the tissue under the skin in consequence of passive hypermania or by the organs in the pit of the stomach or chest. Flabby stomach muscles cause weariness and a slight lowering of the inner organs, as do difficulty in breathing and abnormal blood distribution.

Examination shows that the fascia around the muscles and the capsules enclosing the inner organs (kidneys, liver, etc.) are very rich in the same thin nerve fibres which conduct the secondary protopathic skin pain. Working muscles absorb liquid and swell;

53

when they are taut, the fascia and the ligaments are extended. Even where there is but very slight swelling of the inner organs, as in the case of pathological states or poisoning, sensations are released from the capsules and ligaments. What we call tiredness is nothing but a deep-set, constant, pseudo-painfulness, which is not very intense and resembles a feeling of heaviness or inability.

If this conception is correct, then the stimulation of the inner pain nerves—presuming that this is not intense—has the same function as the slight skin pain known as itch. Physiological significance can be attributed to slight pain or, better, to the stage prior to 'genuine' pain, and to particular forms of stimulation such as those aroused by the stimulation of pain fibres. Even if skin pain is meaningless, the *pain fibres*, like all morphological elements in the body, are functionally meaningful.

Appearing in the form of weariness and forcing us to rest, the antecedent of pain, like pain sensation itself, is characterized by its heaviness and helplessness. Rest can therefore be regarded as the adequate expression of feeling. If we do not give way to the feeling coming from within our body, it may develop into genuine pain. Simple examples illustrate the truth of this statement. Weizsäcker's assertion is noted in this respect as well: 'Painfulness is what we neglect to do.'[41]

Weizsäcker was actually writing of another aspect of the relationship between pain and movement, namely acute sciatica or ischias following a leg fracture. Patients cured of their illness continue to complain of 'rheumatic' muscular pains which the doctors generally regard as after-effects of illness and treat as such. But here the anomaly ends. For Weizsäcker considers that these pains are in actual fact a 'second' illness, which, although it succeeds the first, has a totally different cause, namely the patient's failure to be able to perform his normal duties. In other words, the phase of recovery is governed by a personal attitude expressed in the apparatus of movement. Claims which exceed the patient's powers affect his will so that he finally is unable to make the effort and in fact does not wish to. This is true of all neurotic complaints where functional harmony is disturbed. The result is pain. Pain is the equivalent of non-performance of something which is required. The only treatment for such chronic muscular pain, misnamed 'rheumatic', is 're-education'—especially by means of relaxation therapy. This example shows that pain cannot be explained by means of some process on the periphery, like a stimulation, which is then conducted to a particular part of the nervous system. A personal factor is always responsible too. 'A theory of pain cannot exist which contents itself with a guiding principle derived from the periphery.'

We know from our own experience that *rest* tends to relieve pain and that its effectiveness increases in the degree in which the muscles are relaxed. It is only partly correct to say that rest acts as a preventative against upset and shock, that is, further hurt to the affected area. This may be true in the case of a leg fracture, but it is less so of burns. An explanation has still to be found why rest should relieve neuritis, migraine, etc.; though the fact is undisputed.

In my opinion all these simple facts point to the underlying principle of the phenomenon of pain, namely the relationship already mentioned between self and body. If a person allows his muscles to relax completely and lies without stirring in a quiet room in the dark, we know that the result is not merely a state of inner rest, but actually a strange lack of feeling accompanied by an absence of consciousness although the person is not actually unconscious.

On the basis of this experience, two scientists have evolved a method of producing *complete* relaxation of the skeletal muscles. The means is simply systematic exercise. In his book *Progressive Relaxation* Jacobson[44] has described his experience and Schultz has done the same in his *Das Autogene Training*, with its sub-title *System einer konzentrativen Selbstentspannung.*[45]

Unlike the American, Schultz associated his exercises with Yoga technique. Both writers recommend their therapy for general nervous restlessness, neuroses, and cramp in the inner

55

organs. Although we do not intend to discuss the works of these writers in detail we must note their agreement that complete muscular relaxation can only be achieved by methodical exercise: it is the only way to arrive at the desired *active* relaxation. The psychogenic effects become apparent in the course of the exercise. These effects are the strange absence of consciousness and disappearance of all inner (emotional) movements and tension.

For Yoga technique itself we refer briefly to Max Scheler's interesting observations. *Wesen und Formen der Sympathie*[46] contains a short and clear description of the essentials of Yoga technique. 'Yoga technique "desingularizes" and universalizes "pure life" in man: it enables him to regard the body as the self-alienated *object* of consciousness and the *scene* of the universal life stream which permeates all living beings.' Scheler emphasizes the fact that the sensation of pain is only possible where there is a certain amount of involuntary and automatic but at the same time spontaneous realization coupled with the 'tendency to resist'. The will must assert its dominance over the psychic 'vital' centre which is the seat of *all* involuntary and impulsive awareness. When this has been achieved the spontaneous 'resistance', which is hitherto completely involuntary and unaffected by the mind, becomes susceptible to influence and can be got rid of. The sensation of pain follows suit—as is to be seen in the technique practised by the Fakirs. The art of keeping perfectly still and enduring is really a form of supreme mental activity. It can also be applied, *mutatis mutandis*, to feelings of displeasure at far lower levels.

Our normal attitude to the outer world is formed through the medium of the body. The body involuntarily shares in movements, effected by itself or by other agents in its own organs, which characterize all 'activity'. Although we are not concerned with our own body but with the outside world, our 'nerves' are all tense, that is, our physical sensibility and resonance are acute. Contact with our milieu, and at the same time the 'sense of body' as the means of this contact, are dissolved by relaxation. Our awareness of our own body disappears as our consciousness ceases to be active.

Even without much practice it is easy to see how relaxation of our muscles allows us to forget we have a body. It causes pain to decrease and disappear. Pain is hurtful only because it is a state of conflict between some part of our body and the centre of our personality. It is therefore less when the injured parts of the body are 'forgotten' by the application of various 'techniques'. Similarly, too, any tense psychic activity or excitement, as in battle, or an acute sensory impression or tension of muscles or scream for help, occupies our mind and makes us unaware of pain. It is not correct to assert, as many do, that distracting stimuli draw our attention away from pain in all these instances. The correct interpretation must be placed on the relationship between a person and his own body. Pain is the sensation of crisis and tension, where our normal relationship with our body seems to be destroyed, while it asserts itself in protest in one of its parts. We are conscious of the fact that the injured part belongs to us, but we are incapable of *adequate* reaction. We must do something and we say to ourselves over and over again: 'Painfulness is what we neglect to do.' One of the means to counteract this tension, some definite act, is relaxation, rest, the *somatic equivalent of composure*.

Medical science is aware of the need for getting rid of tension before pain can be relieved. Internal pains are often accompanied by contraction of the smooth inner muscles. If the cramp can be got rid of, pain is lessened and even removed. Many pharmaceutical devices for relieving pain, such as opiates, owe their effectiveness to their power to conduce relaxation and sleep.

Hardy's[47] experiment in measuring fluctuations in the pain threshold by determining the strength of a ray of heat necessary to cause a sensation of pain in the skin has established this fact. The threshold alters by 35 per cent after applying 0·3 gr. (or more) aspirin. The threshold can be raised up to 50 per cent with codeine and up to 100 per cent with morphine (30 mg.). A stimulus which is twice as strong now appears to be of the same intensity as a normal painful stimulus. This does not explain the common pain-soothing effect of morphine, even in much smaller doses (5-10 mg.). Furthermore, the test showed that pain preceding the dose can greatly reduce and even nullify the effectiveness of morphine. Opiates cause the muscles to relax, they bring about apathy, sleep, restfulness, and get rid of fear. Therefore the patient's *reaction* to pain undergoes a change. Hardy reaches the conclusion that morphine and other opiates nullify the usual 'withdrawal—fight—flight—anxiety—reaction pattern of pain' and dissociate the sensation of pain from the reaction to it. These experiments show the close connexion between pain and activity and the significance of the personal attitude in actually feeling pain.

(iv) CENTRAL INFLUENCES ON PAIN

'The element of pain can apparently be modified by changes inside the organism without modification of the stimulus.'

PIÉRON[48]

The intensity of the pain sensations, as we have repeatedly emphasized, depends on numerous conditions. Apart from purely *peripheral* conditions, such as temperature, circulation, and the chemical state of the stimulated part, we can say that pain is *centrally* affected. In physiology this refers to all influences proceeding from the central nervous system and in particular from the brain. Included in these are the somatic processes by means of which all psychic influences on pain arise. The physiological process is something more than stimulus, transmission, and effect, and we cannot attribute the instability of this sequence to purely psychological 'disturbances'. The physical functions are highly organized, and any minor alteration of the conditions causes a change in apparently elementary processes. Every physiological effect owes its consistency to the balance of the functions and not just to the functioning of an isolated anatomical structure.

It need not surprise us that the findings of physiological examination merely confirm our own experience. An experiment disrupts the unity of the organism; it is possible to establish the effects of stimulation or extirpation of a specific part of the nerve. What is not shown is the functional interrelationship under normal conditions. At the very most the experiment can give some indication of how this works, as when certain reactions are examined and their appearance in the body explained. It is still uncertain when or why these occur.

In the case of man, pathological disturbances and injuries to the central nervous system acquaint us with functional and behaviour anomalies. As with animal tests, these can throw light on the conditions governing pain sensations.

Electrical stimuli to the cortex cannot produce a painful sensation.[49] Undefined touch impressions, feelings of movement, occasionally even paraesthesias (irritations), have been established where a specific field in the cortex is stimulated after exposing the surface of the brain for operation. Yet the cortex does influence the manner in which pain sensation is experienced. If an animal's brain is removed its sensitivity to pain is greatly reduced. Isolated clinical cases confirm the importance of the cortex for the manner in which pain is experienced. Agnosia for pain has been registered in cases of injuries to the cortex where the reaction to pain sensation is abnormal.

At any rate there is no such thing as a 'pain centre', and it is not known which parts of the central nervous system are responsible for pain. According to one thesis, pain is perceived in that part of the brain stem known as the thalamus since it is 'responsible' for violent pain in pathological anomalies. Neurological evidence still resists unified treatment, though the work of several scientists points to the opinion that the cortex exercises a regulative influence on the thalamus and that this checks the sensation of pain. In Weizsäcker's[41] view the neuroanatomical basis of the doctrine of pain remains extremely questionable. Physiologists today have demonstrated that elementary functions are not localized. Lesions are followed by functional changes, for these create new relationships between the remaining parts of the nervous system. The extent of the interdependence of pain and the nervous system is not yet established: some parts of the latter are more important than others. One of these is undoubtedly the thalamus. In 1937 the neurologist Stenvers, an expert on the anatomy of the central nervous system, reached the significant conclusion that: 'Anatomy leaves room for all sorts of speculation.' For a pain irritant to cause a pain sensation there must be a whole system of functional conditions, as animal experiments and clinical investigations have shown.[50]

In an experiment the scientist tries to arrive at a maximum number of results that can be reproduced. The conditions are so selected that the same irritant produces the same effect. The extensive 'system of functional conditions' is incalculable and as such is excluded as far as possible. However, in establishing the threshold of pain in the case of man, the dependence of pain sensation in natural life on central influences is illustrated by indirect means. Among others, Hardy's[51] exact measurements proved an important fact, namely that the sensitivity to pain of the skin of 150 persons varied only by approximately 1 per cent. This was independent of sex, mood, and subjective opinion of pain sensitivity. This result appears to contradict the notion of different degrees of sensitivity to pain. For it is believed that primitive races are less sensitive than cultivated, men more so than women, and even that intellectual training results in increased susceptibility. According to Hardy's work these differences—if they exist at all—must be attributed to differences in the *reaction* to pain. So-called sensitive natures react more strongly, or, to put it differently, the same sensation of pain produces in them a greater pathic effect. It is impossible to explain how this comes about. Perhaps the causes are constitutional or 'chemical' (hormonal) divergencies; certainly central conditions and general differences in experiencing one's own corporeality contribute.[52]

An experiment by one of Pavlov's students, Erofeew, provides a good example of the dependence of pain on central conditions. This point will be dealt with more extensively here since it shows how the reaction to pain is governed by the 'pre-history' of the individual. Pavlov and his students are well known for their work on animal behaviour, of which the following is an example: If a dog is repeatedly given food after it has received a sense impression of light, for example, or sound, saliva continues to appear even if the sense irritant alone is given. Russian scientists explain this reaction to the 'signal' in terms of a scheme of conditioned reflexes. They assume that a new path is created in the nervous system which connects the sense impression via the cortex with the centre for secretion of saliva.[53] The dog reacts to the pain irritant with a *reflexe de défense* and this increases in proportion to the intensity of the pain. The defensive reaction consists in a flight movement and other physiological phenomena, such as dilated pupils.

Erofeew combined the feeding with a vigorous electrical stimulation of the skin. After repeating this a number of times she found that instead of an escape movement and dilated pupils, the pain irritant also aroused secretion of saliva and licking of the lips, signs that food was expected. She achieved similar results by varying the pain irritant, burning or pricking injuries, which drew blood, but not if deeper injuries were inflicted. Pavlov concluded from this that, biologically, the most important reflex predominates. Slight injuries do not hinder a dog from seizing his prey whereas a threat to his life puts him to flight; similarly, a hierarchy of reactions can be established by means of experiment. Yet it does not explain why the pain irritant is ineffective. We do not know what goes on inside the animal nor do we know how the processes in the central nervous system can suppress the sensations of pain. But Erofeew's experiment offers incontestable proof of the principle that pain is dependent on a system of central conditions.

Physiologists therefore no longer regard pain as being simply and exclusively determined by the intensity of the irritation (requiring an intact path of pain fibre) and by a pain centre the location of which is not known. Only very vigorous irritations seem to be able to prevent functional elimination of pain, although the opposite is proved by experiments on human beings in connexion with trauma. In the case of major operations which used to be performed without a narcotic, it was noted that pain went through a maximum phase of intensity and then disappeared.

The influence of the central regulation system is known from clinical work dealing with recurrent pain, which is not a symptom of disease, but actually itself a disease. We have in mind here facial pains (neuralgia of the trigeminal nerve) and attacks of headaches on one side of the head, or migraine. The extreme variability and incalculable nature of the attacks are well known, equally so the questionable effect of surgical treatment of trigeminal neuralgia. The attacks, especially with migraine, can have several causes; they can even appear in place of other pains or disease. The causes of the attack can be both physical and psychical, and hereditary and constitutional factors also contribute; according to Weizsäcker, even one's personal life often has some connexion with it. All this helps to prove that it is impossible to construct a simple theory of how such pains originate; it can only be said that a large number of separate phenomena are expressed in a single, apparently simple, result (the attack of migraine). An affliction like a headache can be attributed to the most divergent causes: shortsightedness, tumour of the brain, stomach upset, tiredness, or personal worry.

Thus the composition of a system of central influences includes somatic and psychic phenomena and states, constitutional factors, besides the most delicate nuances of one's personal attitude, expectations, fears, wishes, and memories. This all goes to emphasize the special position of pain not only among the sense impressions but also in the scale of feelings.

(v) PAIN AND THE SYMPATHETIC NERVOUS SYSTEM

'The sympathicus is the main pain nerve.'
LERICHE

The sympathetic nervous system consists of a centrifugal system, leading from the centre to the periphery, whereby influences originating in the spinal cord and the higher elements of the nervous system penetrate to the inner parts of the body and regulate their functions. This is an independent activity and is therefore called autonomic; it only regulates the functions of organs which do not directly influence an animal's relationship with its surroundings. The latter relationships are composed of perceptions and acts which are carried out by the sense organ, the muscles and their connexions in the spinal cord and the brain. This element of the nervous system is known sometimes as the somatic as against the vegetative nervous system. This regulates the heart beat and the width of the bronchi, the peristaltic motion, the secretion of the glands, assimilation in the tissues, and the width and permeability of the smaller blood vessels. Secretion of perspiration, the moisture content in the tissue under the skin, colour and warmth of the skin surface, state of the cells and the hair, and many other skin processes, are all influenced by this nervous system.

The sympathetic system is made up of cells and their fibres. Extremely fine cell-ramifications are to be found in every part of the body. A closely woven network of these fine fibres are also to be found in the skin, in the capsules of the inner organs, the walls of the blood vessels, the joint surfaces, etc., which suggests a certain interdependence of pain and sympathetic innervation.

Centripetal fibres conduct stimulations from the periphery to the central nervous system. These are intermingled with a maze of centrifugal fibres in all organs and tissues. Morphologically they are considered part of the somatic nervous system, on the basis of their progress and the way which they enter the central nervous system; functionally, however, they belong to the vegetative nervous system.

It is conceivable that under normal physiological conditions these pain fibres should have a share in the sympathetic regulation of the vegetative processes. An abnormal irritation would be necessary to cause pain. Although this hypothesis is attractive, it lacks sufficient proof, despite Rein's having established in 1939 the existence of a reflex regulation of metabolism.[54] But the thin nerve fibres may have another function if it is true that their stimulation causes sensations which affect human and animal behaviour. As we have seen, such sensations would amount to weariness.

Clinical work supplies the best evidence of a connexion between the sensation of pain and the sympathetic nervous system. Higier (1926)[55] gave forty-four different reasons in favour, although many of these are not convincing. He is, however, right in drawing attention to the following:

(a) Interference with pain sensation in the skin is often accompanied by changes in the state of nutrition and the bloodstream, which are influenced by the sympathetic nervous system. This is not the case where feeling of pain remains intact and only the sense of touch is disturbed.

(b) Many (protopathic) pains, e.g. in the intestines or the blood vessels, or neuralgic attacks, can be accompanied by vegetative phenomena; these are disturbances in circulation, vomiting, sweating, and emotions such as fear, restlessness, depressions, which are partially related to reactions of the sympathetic nervous system.

(c) Operations performed on the sympathetic nervous system often result in increased sensitivity to pain. As long ago as 1851 Claude Bernard found that he could cause a rabbit to be more sensitive to pain by severing the sympathetic nerve of its ear. Similar observations were made on other animals and on human beings.[56]

Among physicians, the French surgeon Leriche[57] has also indicated the connexion between pain and the autonomic nervous system. Leriche regards the sympathetic as 'the main pain nerve', differentiating between two forms of pain: 'cerebrospinal' and 'sympathetic' pain. The former is well localized and not continual; it does not radiate; its connexion with the irritation is obvious. The localization and extension of 'sympathetic pain' is less easy to ascertain; it is diffuse and radiates over a wide area; it is strongly affected by emotions and other factors, even climatic ones. Nearly all clinical pains belong to this group and therefore vary individually; they are modified by care, medicaments, and suggestion. Sympathetic pain is not easy to study experimentally in the laboratory; its function is probably best investigated in the clinic. The fluctuating character of attacks of migraine or facial pains, incalculable and undefined intestine pains, would suggest interaction with the vegetative nerves. This interaction, however, is so arbitrary that there is a total lack of rules and experimental data on the subject.

The sympathetic nervous system can also affect pain *indirectly*. The centrifugal influences on the smooth muscles in the wall of the intestines, the excretory ducts, the glands and especially in the wall of the blood vessels can increase or reduce pains in the deeper-lying parts of the body. Thus surgical pain therapy tries section of the sympathetic nerve, although with varying success.[58] Causalgia, so-called, a scathing, burning pain, provides an excellent example for the indirect influence of the sympathetic nervous system on pain. In the words of Verbeek:

'in the case of a slight trauma of tissues, whether affecting a nerve or a blood vessel or not, the pains attack the tissue like fire, without respect for anatomical boundaries of the element in question. The pains are accompanied by speedy trophic disturbance of the skin. In the case of persons who develop a characteristically supersensitive psyche in a very short time, these pains are probably due to a disturbance of the sympathetic nervous system.'[59]

Pain and local contraction are often mutually dependent, as for example in the case of the blood vessels or the intestines, or a sphincter muscle, or excretory duct. If one of the phenomena is eradicated, the other follows suit. Pains radiating to the skin from diseased inner organs are dependent on the sympathetic nervous system.[60] Finally a very important proof of this dependence has been furnished by the change that the electrical and exactly measurable stimulation of the receptors in the skin undergoes after section of the autonomic, centrifugal nerve of the appropriate point of the skin.[61]

Allowing for certain unclarified points, we can sum up by saying that the nerves which communicate pain are geared to the elements responsible for vegetative functions, especially the metabolic processes. Without any doubt this is true of the slow-conducting thin fibres which cause the second pain sensation already mentioned. The close connexion between pain and the sympathetic nervous system and thereby with processes in the inner organs confirm our view that pain is not a sensory perception.

(vi) VEGETATIVE REACTIONS TO PAIN

'The most significant feature of the bodily reactions in pain is that they are of the nature of reflexes.'   CANNON[62]

A doctor, or anyone with sufficient opportunity of observing expressions of intense pain among human beings, must be struck by their resemblance to expressions of anger or fear. We shall discuss their effect on breathing and utterance at a later stage. At the moment we are concerned with alterations in the vegetative processes which are caused by pain irritants. These can be observed at the sick-bed and in the case of injured persons; furthermore, they have been analysed in repeated tests on animals. The American physiologist Cannon has made a major contribution to this analysis: he has examined in detail the relationship between pain reactions and vegetative manifestations of anger and fear. In this he was following the method of certain psychologists, and since he made these tests over twenty-five years ago no further new results have been achieved.

Any of us can observe how pain, anger, and fear 'affect the stomach', that is, diminish our appetite. Experiments on animals show that the alimentary canal is extremely sensitive to unpleasant excitement and pain irritants, and that it reacts by reducing secretions from the stomach and other digestive juices.

When at rest the muscles of the intestines, and generally those of the stomach, contract rhythmically. These are known as 'peristaltic motions' which knead and forward their content. By filling the alimentary canal with a non-harmful substance which X-rays cannot penetrate, it is possible to observe the motions by screening. If the animal gets afraid or excited in the course of the observations, or if it becomes angry, the motions immediately stop and sometimes do not recur for hours after. A pain irritant has a similar effect. By means of an opening in the stomach, known as a 'fistula', which receives the secreted fluid, it is possible to measure the effect of fear and anger on the secretion of the stomach juices. These tests have also showed how far excitement and pain causes an animal's (dog's) secretion to stop.

How can the functioning of stomach and intestines be checked by pain irritants? In a series of ingenious tests Cannon showed that anger, fear, and pain bring about increased secretion of adrenalin into the bloodstream; this substance is formed in the adrenals: it causes motions and secretions in the alimentary canal to decline. It was also shown that the increase of adrenalin in the blood following pain irritants was just as great if use was made of narcotics as it was when the animal's brain was removed. The conclusion drawn from this was that secretion of adrenalin is a reflex, that is, automatic and unconscious, and that it does not depend so much on the feeling of pain as on the pain irritant itself.

The 'reflexive' effect of a pain irritant has further direct and indirect influences on other organs. First, blood pressure rises, primarily as a result of contraction of the smallest arteries in the organs of the stomach. The blood vessels in the skeletal muscles and in the heart muscle expand; circulation is quickened. Thus the secretion of adrenalin in pain increases the performance of the heart and the skeletal muscles. This substance stimulates the activity of the heart, and probably also the sensitivity of the muscles, while tired muscles function better. Two further effects of pain, anger, or fear are increased fluidity of the blood and content of blood sugar. All these changes can be attributed for the most part to the effects of adrenalin.

As Cannon continually emphasizes, all these effects are extremely *salutary*. They can be classed together as an 'effort-syndrome', a group of processes all serving to increase activity. In order to understand the purposefulness of the vegetative reactions to pain it must be kept in mind that pain in the animal

68

world is always the occasion of greater tension of the muscles, flight, or attack. This was pointed out by Darwin himself.

Thus pain and affects such as fear and anger are associated with a number of changes in the body: these are the *preliminaries* to intense effort. Digestion ceases and the blood is diverted to the muscles from the digestive system. The heart is stimulated, blood pressure raised and the supply of sugar to the muscles increased, etc. This is all automatic; it is the unconscious and purely physical effect of stimulation of the pain nerve. Such are the results of tests made by Cannon and others.

Secretion of adrenalin, which is responsible for a large number of the effects, can also occur when a pain nerve is irritated under narcosis. Here there is no sensation. The whole salutary effect would thereby have nothing to do with the feelings of pain.

Is this view correct? The tests showed that if an animal is under narcosis the stimulations must be far stronger. This is not the crucial point, however. As we have yet to see, a painful stimulus can be associated with a variety of emotional states and expressive reactions. We can therefore presume that the predominating effect in the tests on animals, the secretion of adrenalin, represents only one type of reaction to pain. This is supported by physiological experiments. It was discovered that pain sometimes caused a lowering of the blood pressure intead of the reverse; in a footnote Cannon stated that it can have not a stimulating, but a depressive, effect. It depends on several conditions and on the quality of the pain.

'Conceivably there is a relation between recognizing the possibility of escape (with the psychic consequences of that possibility) and the degree of stimulating effect. Thus pains originating from the interior of the body, or from injuries sure to be made more painful by action, would probably not lead to action. On the other hand, the whip and spur illustrate the well-known excitant effect of painful stimuli.'

Physiological analysis of the vegetative reactions to pain can only provide a *scheme* of the highly differentiated phenomena which are the natural effects of pain. This emphasizes the importance of making the whole pattern of individual behaviour the basis of discussion and explanation of the experimental physiological data.

III

Pain and Animal Life

(i) HOW AN ANIMAL FEELS PAIN AND WHAT ITS REACTIONS ARE

*'Pain as a sensory signal shows a tendency
to express itself in angry movements of the
limbs. This in its turn causes the subject to
become analgetic.'* R. BILZ[63]

W E CAN never know the emotional life of a being which
does not speak our language. Yet even a complete
mastery of language allows little more than a superficial acquaintance with feelings. This is particularly true of
sensations of pain since their intensity and quality are extremely
difficult to describe. A doctor needs long experience before he
can form an idea of the patient's pain from his disjointed des-
criptions. His opinion is formed by comparing other cases and
circumstances which he has experienced, and above all by his
being able to assess the importance of arbitrary or apparently
arbitrary reactions in the patient—groans or tears, facial expression, tension of the muscles, and general behaviour and movement. What a patient says is not enough to demonstrate that he
has the sensation of pain, but must be used in conjunction with
objectively determined phenomena. The patient's involuntary
expressions of pain can even contradict what he says. Even the
expressive reactions themselves, however spontaneous they may
appear, must be verified in a much larger context. This context is

71

the relationship to the actual cause of pain, to reactions observed in other cases, as well as all data relating to the emotional life, character, and circumstances of the person in question. A doctor, and even less a layman, rarely accounts for the numerous factors which contribute to the formation of his opinion, unless there should be some disagreement with the patient or if the course of the illness proves his diagnosis to be incorrect. Or it may happen that added knowledge of the psychic life of the individual causes him to modify his views.

It is even more difficult to ascertain pain sensations in those whose expressive reactions differ from our own. Examples of these are mental patients, those suffering from grave illness, or members of another race. It is not easy to decide to what extent a newborn baby is sensing pain when it cries or resists treatment. As the child grows, its clarity of consciousness increases, and so it is difficult to defend the thesis that the intensity of conscious experience can be gauged by the reactions it seems to evoke. Children born without a cerebrum (anencephaly) react vigorously. And yet we cannot speak of pain sensation in this case, since there are numerous reasons to prove that consciousness and therefore emotional experience are connected with the functioning of the cerebrum.

All this serves to make us aware of the difficulty of ascertaining pain sensation among animals. On the other hand we cannot say that animal emotional life is a closed book for us or that we have no understanding at all of their sensations of pain. In principle the same factors determine the degree of certainty with regard to animal pain as to the pain of the mentally ill and of children.

We form our opinion of the pain sensation of strangers and animals on more or less a similar basis; in the former case we are at an advantage in that we are far better acquainted with the psychic structure of a human being and the conditions which determine it. In fact our assessment of the intensity and even the quality of pain can be very reliable in so far as the persons and circumstances are 'normal'. That this is not so with animals is not because we may dispute the application of an analogy between man and animal, despite current opinion. The cause lies rather in the difficulty of assessing the degree of clarity of consciousness which an animal enjoys and because the physiological analysis depends on varied conditions.

Before pursuing inquiries into the question of pain sensation among animals, we must first discuss their consciousness and emotional life in general. Here the distinction between lower and higher animal orders must be borne in mind. A high animal, so-called, is not necessarily one that is better built or accommodated to its surroundings; it is not even one more highly differentiated.[64] It belongs to the higher order in so far as it represents the idea of animal existence more completely. It is more independent of its surroundings and can be said to have a definite attitude to things. Its animal function operates in a framework of time and place, of formed impressions and individual experience. This can all be summarized in three concepts: 'intelligence', differentiated relationships, and greater degree of control over its own body (apart altogether from bodily functions). It has accordingly been thought that higher animals have a greater degree of consciousness; this view disregarded the fact that the development of bodily structure does not always correspond to a difference in function and behaviour. An animal's position in the zoological scale is no measure of the clarity of its consciousness. Man's consciousness grows from the day of his birth in extent, depth, and clarity. It moves in ratio to his associations with his surroundings. At first the child reacts to simple sensory impressions. It is protected from conflict and experiences no resistance. It does not need to defend itself, and so it does not react to forms or distances; it has no formed habits nor differentiated actions. This type of existence is one of dormant consciousness.

If we compare the conditions under which an animal lives with the stages of human development, that is, not the details, but

73

the general character of its relationship with its immediate surroundings, we are forced to the conclusion that, *formally* speaking, many zoologically lower animal orders react to the world
around them as a newborn child, or even an embryo. Consciousness among such animals is dim. Then there are other lower
animals furnished with an extensive scale of finely differentiated
reactions to situations. Formally, the behaviour of such animals
can be compared to that of an older child; in principle it does not
differ from the actions of higher animals. Thus among the lower
animals there are the hunters, which lie in wait for their prey at
a distance, creep up and spring on it, pursue and fight with strong
opponents or flee from them; in other words they constantly
accommodate their actions to the structure of the hunting or
fighting area. A good example of highly developed relationship
to the surroundings among the lower orders is the octopus,
a type of cuttle fish. Its behaviour is more differentiated than
that of many vertebrates, which exist in a 'dream' and do not
react to animals of prey, but only to food areas, climatic
influences, and, at most, to others of their species.[65] The
consciousness of the octopus might be said to be clearer than
that of the carp or even the cow.

Our judgment must be cautious, none the less. Experience of
our own psychic life teaches us that differentiated actions can
also be performed without the subject's being aware of their
course, and habits can be formed and things perceived or
recognized without conscious realization. We possess criteria as
to the clarity of human consciousness other than mere differentiation of surroundings, namely reasonable consideration and
emotions.

Reasonable consideration is ascertained on the basis of perceptible behaviour. There are actions which are *more* than mere
reactions to the particular situation, more than habits based on
definite experiences. This type of action can only be explained
by the subject having *consciously* 'considered'. It is to be found
neither in lower nor in higher orders.[66] *Expressive movements*

74

indicate the presence of emotions. These are to be found both among humans and among animals[67] and must be carefully examined in order to be able to assess the feeling of pain. A painful stimulus is answered in a certain manner, just as it is felt in a certain manner. The emphasis is on the *'certain manner'*, since tests on animals and clinical experience have both proved that unconscious reflexes can also follow a painful stimulus. But these are not expressive movements.

Apart from the difference between unconscious reflex motions and those which constitute an expression of feeling, there is a further difference to be noted, namely between emotional expression and the starting position of an action.

Emotional states occur as a result of some act being checked or delayed by circumstances, e.g. flight or attack. In this case the impulse finds expression in another manner. The expressive movement *represents* the intention to act; it is not, as Darwin believed, a part or a remainder of the action itself. Such representative motions and activities almost certainly indicate an emotion. In the case of an animal, it is legitimate to assume at the same time the presence of a conscious feeling. But the difficulty lies in ascertaining whether this is an expressive motion or an unconscious reflex or even the starting position of an act, which responds to the situation in the desired manner.

In the lower orders the state of affairs is clear. Here we meet the starting position only, for flight or concealment, attack or defence. We usually explain these incorrectly as expressive movements. What we observe in an insect, shrimp, spider, snail, or even an octopus, when confronted with danger is but the initial phase of a reaction and *not a representation of this*. There is thus a great difference between the reaction of a cat with dilated pupils, its fur standing on end and its tail in the air, spitting at an approaching dog, and a shrimp opening its claws or a wood ant its jaws and raising itself to parry possible attack.

It is not always easy to distinguish between expressive movements and the automatic incipient position of an act. In many

75

cases it is impossible to be quite certain. However, the more one knows about the behaviour of an animal order in varying circumstances the more surely can one ascertain the quality of its emotional life and expression. The existence of positive feelings such as desire, joy, devotion, consideration, and expectation among dogs and cats give us evidence to support the existence of negative feelings as well. There is a complete lack of positive feeling in the lower orders. To imagine that a wasp expresses 'anger' by buzzing louder on being waved away from the sugar bowl or that fishes are 'frightened' when they dive if a stone is thrown into the water is a superficial analogy.

Before determining the existence of a feeling of pain among animals, it is first necessary to clarify the distinction between feeling and *genuine* expressive movement. This can only be done by studying animal reaction to strong harmful stimuli.

To take the lower animals first. Reactions to strong stimuli, injuries, chemical irritations, burns, etc., are usually of two kinds: flight and disorganization. In many cases there is unexpectedly no reaction at all.

Flight movements are fairly widespread on the whole. These consist of withdrawal of the affected part or of the whole body. This reaction is particularly frequent where the stimulus is slight. It is certainly no evidence that pain is felt. If the brain is removed, e.g. in a decapitated frog or eel, the flight movements are just as pronounced. Physiologists rightly class as unconscious reflexes such things as drawing together the extremities, contraction of the skin or bending the rump to one side. As tests show, there is a certain ratio between the strength of the stimulus and the speed and extension of the flight movement, but this is very dependent on circumstance, on the place and nature of the stimulus. Sensitive organs, like feeler hairs, can react to very slight, non-harmful stimuli, whereas in other parts the stimuli must cause serious injury before a reflex appears. Thus there is frequent disparity between the reaction to pain and the extent of the injury inflicted, while the influence of circumstances is also very great. For

76

example, a frog snaps at a fly placed between two needles till its tongue is badly cut, yet if its jaws are stimulated unexpectedly, it reacts by flight.

Vigorous stimuli among lower animals arouse violent defensive movements resulting in kinetic *disorganization*, rolling over and sprawling, similar to chaotic reactions among humans and higher animals in such situations. This is the very form of reaction commonly held to be an expression of pain and proof of the existence of a feeling of pain. I do not believe this is true. Even among decerebrate animals strong continuous stimulation causes flight reaction to give place to kinetic disorganization. The correct interpretation, in my opinion, is that the boundaries of the physiological functional nexus are severed. The strong stimuli are therefore able to spread themselves without any obstacle throughout the nervous system.

This must be the explanation of Norman's well-known observation on the worm. If the animal is cut in two, the headless back part curls 'in pain' while the front part keeps crawling. This is taken to show that this animal has no sense of pain, whereas in reality all that the experiment shows is that the creature is incapable of co-ordinated movement. Lower animals often show no reaction to injury in the back part of their body. It takes some time before they return to normal behaviour after a stimulus has caused a flight movement. In fact there is frequently no flight movement or motor disorganization of the part of the body, whether a foot or the rump, if the amputation takes place quickly. The action may not even be interrupted. The best-known and constantly quoted example is Forel's observation that, like Münchausen's horse, a wasp or an ant, the back parts of which have been amputated, goes on drinking.

These and similar observations have an *indirect* bearing on the problem of pain. They provide evidence of the greater independence of the parts of the body and of the more automatic character of actions among the lower animals. Self-

77

amputation among crabs and some kinds of spiders should be mentioned here: a strong, potentially fatal stimulus makes them 'sacrifice' one or more legs. Similarly there are insects and other articulated animals who inflict injury on themselves, while in the case of others the female injures and even partially swallows the male without interrupting copulation. The reactions of lower animals furnish no evidence of expressive movements, and although there are plenty of emotional arguments for the existence of pain sensation among them, there is no proof of this.

There is one case where a scientist might be inclined to assume the existence of genuine expressive movements and this is the octopus. This animal has human 'eyes' with living pupil reactions. The skin is tightly filled with contractible cells full of a coloured matter known as chromatophores. The matter enables the animal to change colour very rapidly and to great effect, giving an impression of emotional expressive movements. If the animal is endangered, or when it approaches its prey, it becomes dark with 'rage' or 'excitement'. At least so it appears. The variegated reactions already mentioned support the conviction that, functionally speaking, this is a higher animal. We can understand how a good psychologist like Piéron can write of the octopus: 'The pupillary and chromatophoric reactions of the octopus give evidence of pain.'

And indeed among higher animals the reactions of the pupils and the skin organs (hair, feathers, blood vessels) are very closely connected with the emotions: a similar association would appear to be present in the octopus. It is however possible to mistake the true nature of these reactions; physiological tests have proved that vegetative reactions continue to appear after the higher parts of the nervous system have been removed.

We must be acquainted with the reactions of the octopus in the most varied situations in order to determine whether it feels pain or not. Basing my opinion on personal experiments I believe that this mollusc is as highly developed as any of the cold-blooded vertebrates. Pain sensation is therefore most probably present.

We must qualify our opinion in the case of the octopus but not in that of the mammal. This is because of the marked kinship in bodily structure between mammals and humans which allows us to assume a similar application of means to express reaction to pain sensation. Thus a monkey pulls away its paw as a human does when stimulated by heat or electric current, jumping back with a scream; a serious lesion will cause it to keep the injured part quiet or even clutch it tightly. In other words, the elementary and direct reactions of a higher animal to a sudden feeling of pain and flight movement are such that we can *imitate* them. That is why we say that its expressive movements can be felt, that they can be understood.

How does a higher animal react to pain? Even among domestic animals great divergencies can be noted, both of breed and from one individual to another. The latter is particularly important. It confirms our impression that real feelings are expressed and not merely typical reactions of the species.

Our observations, for the sake of simplicity, will be confined to the pain reactions of a dog; five basic forms can be established: (i) flight reactions, (ii) kinetic disorganization, (iii) aggressive expression, (iv) check on its movements, (v) care (and defence) of the injured part. All five forms of reactions may be accompanied by sound utterances.

If a dog's tail or paw is pinched, its reaction is to withdraw it. If it is struck by a stone, it runs away whining. Tests prove that it draws in its extremities before it can possibly have felt pain. But the auditory utterances attest the presence of a pain sensation, and, we feel, rightly so. Whining is a certain mark of the animal's having felt the injury. And yet there is often a relative discrepancy between the animal's whining and the intensity of the injury. Some dogs are hypersensitive and fear usually sharpens the expression of pain. The same is true of

79

human beings: this very analogy helps us to *understand* the animal's utterances as being those of fear and pain.

Grave injuries—as a result of being run over or receiving bad burns—cause not flight but senseless movements or kinetic disorganization. The animal rolls all over the place, runs around whimpering, draws in its extremities, collides with objects, stumbles, etc. Of a human being in this state we would say he 'had gone off his head'. But usually this state does not last long. It develops soon into a chronic state of unrest and subdued whimpering. Humans accommodate themselves and their pain reactions diminish in a similar manner. Indeed the whole image of an injured dog so resembles that of a man that we are convinced that the disorganized excitement of a mammal is evidence of its experience of pain: it is not merely, we feel, the result of stimuli impinging upon the nervous system. In addition the motor disruption is a series of aimless but not unco-ordinated movements. Turbulence and excitement express the need to 'escape' from something, as though the subject had something it was unable to 'get rid of'. We may observe that there are in fact *several* analogous states of excitement expressing this inability to be rid of something. They all show the appearance of restless energy, like some hidden fire. Extreme fear or joy are accompanied by these aimless 'turbulent' movements, and often by various utterances—in the case of a dog, by whimpering. A man with something preying on his mind is, as it were, hurt in spirit: he walks up and down, he gesticulates, sighs, and groans in his unrest, his face often twitching as if in pain.

A dog's disorganized movements correspond to these: they are mere physical reactions, an unordered extension of the stimuli into the central nervous system. Among lower and decerebrate animals this occurs in the form of pseudo-emotional utterance. On the other hand these movements represent *genuine* expressive movements: they are the expression of a feeling from which the individual cannot find release and which *clings* to him obstinately despite all his efforts to shake it off. This is one of the essential characteristics of a sensation of pain, as indicated above (p. 26). The expression of this symptom is the very 'diffuse flight reaction' (v. Gebsattel). Screams, whines, and whimpering are the most characteristic features of the reaction.

We mentioned aggressiveness as the third form of pain reaction. Pain causes rage. We can see this in a dog too. We owe our awareness to the connexion between pain and rage to R. Bilz's study *Pars pro toto*,[63] which also treats the expressive phenomena of the effects with which we are here concerned. In it he relates how he treated his dog for eczema on its tail with ointment. The dog reacted by whimpering and snapping at its own tail as though it were an enemy. Ordinarily a patient and peaceful animal, this treatment aroused violent *emotions* in it. One might have expected it to try and lick the ointment off with an obvious show of pain. That would at least have been a logical action to remove pain, but instead it reacted 'scenically', as though it were biting an enemy inflicting pain on it. All of a sudden it was consumed with activity. Bilz feels that this centrifugal tendency to snap all round it must be regarded as the expression 'of a conflict. The *pain of the injury* presupposes an *adversary*.' Bilz's thesis is confirmed by a number of observations. Even a good-tempered dog can bite its master if it is in pain. But it is doubtful whether this really constitutes a struggle against the 'unknown', or if the analogy which the author draws between the aggressive reaction of man and of a dog is correct. The comparison is significant, however, if we are to *understand* the reaction. It is quite true to say that man becomes irritable in pain, even mad. Every doctor is familiar with this. But it does not follow that the action of a man in grasping the arm of a dentist's chair with all his might or crumpling a handkerchief, or the behaviour of Darwin's sailors, who were said to have bitten into a piece of lead when beaten so as to be able to bear the pain, represent forms of expressing rage.

We must take a simple example in order to understand the reactions of a dog. A sleeping dog is bitten by an insect and it jumps up and snaps at the place where it is stung. This is Bilz's 'conflict scene'. But the dog's action is aimed at a specific point. It is not an expressive movement representing an emotion. The animal has been stimulated at *a certain place*, and although the stimulus is here connected with a painful bite in the skin, the reaction is the same as to any other stimulus, as for example if we hold on to a dog to prevent him from running away. The connexion between stimulus and emotion can possibly be grasped by applying Palagyi's theory of vital phantasy. Our own study of animal movement and play might be mentioned at this point.[68]

A simple example of how an animal's aggressive reaction is an expressive movement and not an action is furnished by the image of a dog lying in great pain in a basket. Its breathing is hurried and it is restless as though, like a human being in the same state, opposing tendencies were at war within it. The above-mentioned fourth reaction, the check on its movements, is also to be observed, the effort to prevent pain by keeping perfectly still. Now and again, when the pain becomes greater, the dog *bites* the edge of the basket in the manner a woman in labour clenches a handkerchief in her teeth between pains. Is this an utterance of rage? Certainly not in Bilz's sense. But in so far as the pain stimulus is dynamically related to an adversary, it is. Pain, as Bilz has quite rightly demonstrated, leads to oral and brachial activity, which is quite different from the actions involved in an 'angry conflict'. Pain is followed by secretion of saliva, also the mark of rage, though in a different form: we 'foam' with rage. Screams and groans of pain are related to, but not identical with, utterances of rage. Pain causes biting or clenching of teeth, rage, grinding (and usually baring) of the teeth. Pain and rage are also conducive to 'brachial' as well as oral activity. A human being moves his arms and legs, a dog its paws. We clench our fist in rage, which, however, is not quite the same as pressing our hands against each other in pain; similarly gestures of rage, stamping, etc., differ from the kinetic

82

restlessness of pain. In an animal we can also distinguish between the differences and the similarities of motions expressing pain and rage.

We can only tell why this is so once we have discovered what is common to both emotions. Besides the common stimulus, both result in a state of 'being beside oneself', in fact of utter helplessness. A human being and an animal can actually become 'mad' with pain as with rage.

But if helplessness can give place to activity by the subject's reasserting itself and regaining control over itself, the basis of pain and rage is automatically destroyed. Bilz says that the individual becomes insensitive (analgetic) to pain when it is fighting. In saying so he is really dealing with 'vital' reactions. This is very obvious in the case of a dog. It means that pain does not exist without helplessness and perplexity, and that when fighting an animal is completely absorbed. Its reactions are now 'vital' ones. It is no longer in full possession of itself and so cannot get 'beside itself'. This is also what is meant by oral and brachial activity in pain, namely the tendency to become absorbed. Nothing is so conducive to this end as aggression, biting, pinching, etc. We must therefore be thoroughly acquainted with these inner relationships of the emotional life in order to understand the nature of pain, and we shall return to consider them in studying the phenomenology of human pain.

An example of the fourth form of such reactions, the check on movements, is illustrated by a dog lying injured or with a broken leg. When we are acquainted with an animal's normal activity, it is easy to see how its movements are hindered (cf. Pain and Movement, p. 52). Our human experience shows us that by keeping the injured part still and remaining generally quiet it is possible to 'forget' that we have a body. As a result the pains which owe their intensity to the conflict between person and body diminish and disappear. This explanation rests on an interpretation of pain as a feeling arising from disturbance in the normal relation to our own body; the body asserts itself independently in its injured state and we are incapable of adequate reaction. Is this explanation true in the case of the animal as well? To answer this question, we must examine the animal's relationship to its own body and its own 'individual centre'.

We assume a difference in principle between human beings and animals, both in relation to the outside world and to their own bodies. This difference has been formulated in many ways, the most exact being that of Plessner[16] with the concepts 'centric' and 'excentric' *positionality* in his book *Die Stufen des Organischen.* He shows that man by nature lives by means of and in his body, like an animal, moving and being moved from its centre. His human nature helps him to transpose his own person outside this 'vital' or psychic centre and place himself face to face with it and accordingly with his body. He is in a position to regard everything taking place through the medium of his body with a certain objectivity. This, the essential nature of man, is the key to the actual and obvious divergencies between man and animal. There is no mental life without excentric positionality, no thinking, willing, language, or culture. In a later work Plessner showed how phenomena which *seem* to be exclusively attributes of bodily nature, like weeping and laughter, have their roots in excentric positionality and are therefore lacking in an animal. These reactions are *not* expressive phenomena but existential crises. The significance of this interpretation lies in the fact that it bases the whole theory of expressive movements and emotional life on an ontological relationship of the body to its subject.

In the course of our study of pain and its expression, we have constantly spoken of this relationship of the subject to its own sense of having a body. We must now discuss whether this is present in the animal world. The fifth reaction form of the dog, care and defence of the injured part, forces us to consider this matter. An excellent description is contained in an article by Prince Auersperg on *Schmerzproblem und vegetatives Nervensystem.*[69] Pain, he says, can develop into a passive state of endurance like the sensation produced by cold hands and feet.

'The experience makes us directly conscious of our injured limbs in their quality as a definite state, which ordinarily takes a back place in our scheme of action.'

'The continual pain attributes a sort of independent existence to the injured part, commending it to our especial protection and care. A dog with a hurt paw looks after it and defends it as it would its young. Nor do we act differently.'

This could not be put better. The dog does nurse and defend its paw as it would its young. But does the painful part become *opposed* to the 'individual centre' as in the case of man? The answer is not to be found by merely observing its behaviour. We see the dog nursing its paw like a mother animal its young. But we must first draw a distinction between the relation of an animal and its young and a mother and her child before we can realize that care in handling a painful part of the body is in no way proof of *excentric* positionality.

Just as an animal is emotionally associated with everything surrounding it, so the mother animal is associated with her young. Specific sensory impressions, as tests demonstrate, are responsible for creating and maintaining this relationship. These are undoubtedly connected with a central emotional resonance, animal feeling, but they cannot be experienced 'objectively'. There is no trace of conscious awareness of feeling which is the characteristic of the *excentric* position. It is an *essential* feature of *all* animal behaviour—and so in the care of the young—that the sensory impressions only acquire their emotional value through the behaviour of the animal—the act of care itself. Being moved and moving form a *single* 'vital' process, in which the animal centre remains *joined* with the object of the surroundings until such time as a sensory or kinetic change causes the process to disintegrate. This is how we are to explain the relationship between the dog and its injured paw, with the difference that in this case the animal is not connected with an object existing outside itself, but with part of its body emotionally associated with it through the medium of its body. The animal experiences its paw in a manner different from usual, whereby, as in the behaviour of all higher animals, *experience* has a share in determining the reaction to impressions, in this case to pain. The dog is taught by experience that if it moves or is moved by some other agency, the pain will be intensified.

This fifth form of reaction is thus part of the 'vital' sphere, corresponding to the centric positionality of the animal. Only if the animal draws the attention of its surroundings to its paw, so to speak, by a suggestive look, e.g. if a monkey should really point to one paw with another, could we be justified in attributing to it an excentric relationship with its own body. The animal would then have passed beyond the boundaries of animal existence and taken the first step on the path of man. For only man experiences the objectivity of things and affects.

Although a dog does certainly experience pain, there is an undoubted difference between its manner of doing so and ours. It does not enjoy freedom with regard to its hurtful sensation, nor the consequent emancipation from the 'vital' pattern of behaviour. And yet it is an interesting fact that a finely differentiated relationship to their own bodies does exist among higher animals and that this is totally lacking in the case of the lower ones. Unfortunately our knowledge of this question is very fragmentary and a systematic study of the distinction in various animal species would respond to a very real need.

Insects, such as beetles, can crawl around even though the back portion of their bodies is partially eaten away. Uexküll[70] asserts that a dragonfly eats its own rump if pinched between the jaws. There are even reports of higher animals with damaged extremities acting in a similar manner. Rats and other animals gnaw off *insensitive* paws, but they lick their wounds. A monkey, however, *feels* a lame or insensitive paw with the others and treats the injured part with even greater care than does a dog. Yet a horse will stay standing on a broken leg and prevents its healing.

It is said of certain water birds that they make a sort of plaster for a broken foot from clay, but we have no positive proof of the reliability of such assertions.

The study of animal behaviour demonstrates that animals feel pain even to the degree of helplessness. Furthermore we learn that pain increases with fear and can vanish in fighting. If a horse is afraid it reacts to the slightest pain stimulus, whereas if it is kept quiet it can be operated on without the smallest reaction. But the *general* properties of animal life show that the pain an animal endures does not cause it to *suffer*. This fact cannot be deduced *directly* from animal behaviour and it is therefore frequently overlooked.

Suffering from pain does not presuppose any explicit reaction, for a child can suffer pain without reflection or verbal utterance. Man cannot get away from his excentric position and he therefore bears pain as something opposed to himself. Pain, which he senses directly, he also endures like any other animal, indirectly in its relationship *to himself*. Such pain lies outside the boundaries of the 'vital' sphere: it is human in the primary sense of the word. Its intensity, quality, and effects are determined by a personal attitude and these, conversely, react on the latter. The *ability* to suffer does not, however, depend on a certain psychological attitude. It is given *in* human existence. '*It is man's privilege to be able to suffer*' (O. Schwarz).[23]

(ii) PAIN AND HABIT FORMATION

> '*Pain does not accompany the formation of
> a habit of function; it only follows it, often
> after a considerable lapse of time . . . and
> cannot therefore prevent it.*' PRADINES[71]

Proverbs like 'Once bitten, twice shy' show that human experience regards pain as a forcible method of accommodating us to

87

our circumstances. This is certainly true of pain caused by injury and, to a certain extent, of pains resulting from our actions. An unpleasant sensation of pain causes us to reflect; our intelligence tries to discern the causes and the occasions of the injury while drawing the conclusion that these are to be avoided in the future. 'The pain receptor must be the judge,' as Pradines says.

It is a long-established fact that all animals learn from unpleasant experiences, but it is scientifically unsound to deduce from this that animals possess understanding and are capable of forming judgments. The relationship of pain to habit formation in the animal world differs from that of the human world. It is this relationship which concerns us here.

We need only glance at the natural world to see the relevance of unpleasant stimuli to the skin and mucous membrane of the mouth in habit formation among animals. Plants have spikes, thorns, and nettle hairs, while numerous animals have nettle organs, bristles, spikes, nails, and teeth. An organism with such an armoury will be avoided by enemies. There seems to be a biological connexion between pain and habit formation in the natural world.

'Punitive stimuli' are often used in training animals to perform various actions. The tamer knows this and his knowledge is constantly being confirmed by his experience that a reward produces better results than punishment. Painful stimuli can only be applied at a certain specific moment. Above all they must not be acute. These observations have been attested in many studies on animal psychology where the conditions of habit formation among lower and higher animals have been more precisely defined.

The most important result of these experiments is to show that animal learning cannot be explained mechanically or neuro-physiologically, for example through the formation of new associations in the nervous system (by tracing out new nerve paths) as a result of frequently repeated combinations of sensory impressions and specific movements. This view was disproved by one of the first theorists of habit formation, the American scholar Thorndike. He explained learning in terms of the 'law of effect' and the 'law of exercise'. In recent decades tame rats have been used in experiments to assess the theory. The rats were forced to learn to choose between two different visual or other sensory impressions or to find a way out of a maze composed of blind alleys and paths, one of which leads to the 'goal' (food or nest). In both types of test 'rewards' and 'punishments' were used, the latter mostly in the form of painful stimuli. The rat would receive an electric shock through its paws if it went the wrong way or made the wrong choice. We shall omit the details of the type of reward, the quantity or quality of the food or the manner in which the mother reached her nest or young. The general result is relevant in this context. It shows that the *result* of the action plays a large part in determining the forming of new habits.

There are far fewer experiments dealing with the significance of painful stimuli for animal learning. As a rule the rat 'punishes' itself if it makes a wrong choice in direction: it comes to a cul-de-sac and is forced to retrace its steps. Painful stimuli can only be applied to advantage if they are sufficiently slight so as not to confuse the animal. It is of further importance that the stimuli be applied at the appropriate moment, that is, if possible, at the very instant when the animal is about to make its choice. If the stimulus is applied too soon or too late, it is without influence on habit formation.

It is not necessary to go into further detail here. A few examples will suffice: a white rat is placed on a board fastened to a stand a little above table level. From this point it can reach two smaller boards somewhat lower down which are slightly separated from one another. They are different in colour, one white and one black. We wish to teach the rat to choose the white one no matter whether it is on the right or on the left. The animal looks down from its first position on to the two smaller boards and after some hesitation it climbs down with its front paws cautiously on to one or other of them. Habit formation can be effected by various means. Either a reward is given each time the rat climbs on to the white board (food or return to the nest), or an unpleasant stimulus, like an electric shock, is administered while the rat is climbing down on to the black board. Both boards are fitted with metal wires and electric current runs through the black one.

The rat can also receive a *non-painful* stimulus. The boards can be mounted so that they revolve as soon as the rat steps on to them. Some obstacle prevents the white board from moving but the black one offers no resistance if stepped on. This method *very quickly* teaches the rat to prefer the white board to the black. Painful stimuli achieve the result less rapidly, since, if an electric shock is strong enough, it causes the rat not to withdraw, but to spring forward quickly. If it is too strong it confuses it, causing kinetic disorganization which interferes with habit formation. It would seem that this could be avoided by diminishing the strength of the stimulus. Yet this is not possible either, for it cannot be determined how 'sensitive' an animal is. Sensitivity varies, probably according to how far the animal's attention is diverted by the situation or its own movements. If the stimulus is too weak it has no influence on the training process, if it is too strong it produces a vigorous reaction, and if repeated the animal's movements become *generally* constricted.

It appears to be true to say that a dog learns by means of painful stimuli, but only in *certain* circumstances, which are very often met with under natural conditions. A dog avoids another dog which has on occasion bitten it. Several further examples illustrate that animals can learn very quickly from a single, unpleasant, if painless, experience. This is true of higher and lower animals alike. If a certain type of food which the animal likes is given to it mixed with some acid substance, the animal will first take it without hesitation but then refuse it for a long time after. Similar tests have been made on toads and spiders and the results prove that even the lower animals learn from unpleasant experiences, even from a single one if it is properly adapted to normal conditions. An animal in the natural world very soon learns to avoid prey with spikes or one containing some burning substance. The tests on toads and spiders enable us to follow the process of habit formation in nature.

Animal learning usually takes place within the set limits of instincts peculiar to each individual species. This means that there are certain characteristic relationships between individuals of a species and their natural environment and it is impossible to form more than a specific number of such relationships. Both these and the animals' reactions to sensory impressions are limited in the 'vital' sphere. This is the first divergence in quality and principle from human learning, which is not similarly restricted. Sensory impressions in the case of animals can assume the character of signals in a specified number of situations. They regulate action by bringing about emotional reactions to situations which are, biologically speaking, significant. Among human beings a sensory impression is more than this: it can be a signal, but it can also be a sign devoid of emotional content, representing something else to the mind.

With the basic character of animal learning in mind we can now examine the connexion between pain and habit formation. To recapitulate: (i) pain is only effective if it is slight and applied at the right moment; (ii) pain, if judiciously applied, leads to withdrawal or flight movements which are reproduced later if the same situation recurs.

Stimuli to the mucous membrane of the skin and mouth are always concerned in the process of habit formation. In the course of our physiological analysis we saw that flight reaction followed a painful stimulus *before* pain was felt. The prick or the sensation of sharpness or heat is felt *during* the actual motion of withdrawal. The pain itself comes later. Pradines is therefore correct when he states: 'Pain does not accompany the formation of a habit or function.' The stimulus to the surface senses, the 'defensive irritation', also found among the lower animals, and not the actual sensation of pain, is functionally important in habit formation. Pain has only a paralysing, disorganizing effect, loosening the bonds between subject and situation and arousing terror, fear, and horror. Stimuli with negative reactions only cause an animal to withdraw as in fear: this is no basis for establishing habit.

If a dog sees a whip with which it has been struck it becomes afraid: its fear is in proportion to the severity of the beating. Yet pain itself is not associated with the optical image of the whip and then reproduced. The animal's reaction proves this. We see it very clearly in the case of a monkey who has had an electric shock and who runs with all appearance of fright, but not of pain, when it sees the instrument which inflicted the shock. Even human beings are unable to recall pain, as we know from experience. A person going to the dentist is afraid and his fear is tempered by the intensity of suffering on previous visits.

We cannot therefore base our explanation of the relationship between pain and habit formation on a supposed association between feeling and activity. Nor is the relationship the same as that of learning by means of reward. In his imagination, a man anticipates a pleasant result in its emotional aspect as something attractive. In the so-called 'vital' spheres there is certainly no clear image of the pleasant result of the action (when performed) but there is a sort of presentiment, which is found among animals too. Without assessing the clearness of consciousness of this 'vital phantasy' (Palagyi) we can say the 'appetite' stimulating the animal to *positive* action is directed towards the future. Where the reaction is negative on account of some previous unpleasant experience, the structure of the psychic process is different. In other words, the animal's reaction in withdrawing and the *fear* emotion aroused in it are caused by its having recognized a situation in which it has once experienced pain, not by the *consequence* of its present action, namely the expected feeling of pain.

A dog, like a human being, trembles with fear on re-entering an operating theatre and hearing the preparatory sounds. The *very perceptions* have the effect of causing alarm. Man can undoubtedly realize that he is going to feel pain but his realization is part of a mental process and therefore emancipated from 'vital' associations. It has nothing to do with spontaneous reactions.

How are we to explain this emotion of fear? It is the after-effect of pain causing the child or animal to avoid contact with objects which have hurt it. It is a sign that the child has obviously learnt something. The answer to the question lies in the experience of pain itself, which is the basis for learning negative reactions. If a person is burnt or stung or receives an electric shock, he does not simply withdraw his hand and allow the, so to speak, peaceful pain which ensues to take its course. This may be true of slight pain. A flight movement is accompanied by the feeling that something 'frightful' is taking place: the vigour of the flight movements and the screams are its expressions. At the actual stage of affliction there is no pain; the fright assimilates itself with the situation in the form of a sensation.

In our phenomenological analysis of the human experience of pain, we shall devote more space to this problem. Here it will be sufficient to say that pain and learning in the animal world are only indirectly connected. An animal that can feel fear and suffer a fright—only the higher animals are capable of this—learns through pain to avoid something: it does not learn to remedy the fright in a positive sense. A fairly strong stimulus is therefore unsuitable as a means of encouraging selective reactions. The only result is that the animal becomes constricted and does not select at all. But all animals are well able to learn to avoid something and to do something else with the aid of a moderately superficial stimulus following certain movements. The negative emotional element is then associated with an *aspect* of the situation: this is possible because it is experienced as a *quality* of this aspect of the environment. The stimulus is didactic, that is, it tells something of the nature of the objects, either that they are sharp, stinging, burning, hot or cold, or pungent. *Genuine* pain, on the other hand, is a state of passive endurance without an object. It is *destructive* and cannot contribute to forming new actions.

(iii) ORIGIN AND PURPOSE OF PAIN

'And so it would appear that pain is not necessary to make us avoid present danger.'
LEIBNIZ.[72]

Genesis is universally acknowledged by modern biologists as the most adequate means of determining the relationships of life phenomena. This concept is very closely associated with that of phylogenesis, or gradual evolution of the species. The theory has been subjected to various alterations and emendations since the days of Lamarck and Darwin, but the principle is still accepted that the higher animals evolved from the lower and that anatomical structure and the functions of the organs are explained by the genealogical tree.

In the last decades, however, the basic principles of biology have changed markedly. Hitherto evolution rested on the ideas of natural selection, variability, and the struggle for existence. To these a further element is added, namely the existence of certain formative influences not derived from other phenomena.[73] It is agreed that 'structural plans' exist for larger groups of organisms which cannot have come into existence independently of one another. Many attributes of the plant and animal world are not the result of a life struggle between variations and mutations because they are not and never can have been important for the preservation of the individual or species.[74]

The genesis of pain allows of two possible interpretations: either a sense of pain evolved, or it is an element of animal existence, and it becomes more pronounced according as the animal realizes its form of existence more fully.

The first of these presupposes that pain is the most adequate alarm signal for an animal in danger. According to Darwin's scheme this would give sensitive animals greater security against danger: their chance of survival would be increased. The preservation of the species would be thereby better assured. The suffering of the individual is therefore an unavoidable evil invested in nature for the sake of the greater good, the triumph of the species. 'Better to suffer than to die.'

One consequence of such an hypothesis is that pain is no more than the sensation caused by a vigorous stimulus whose effect is physical, and is accompanied by a conscious feeling of unpleasantness and a general kinetic and vegetative reaction. Is the effect alone functionally significant? Or are all three accompaniments significant? Only if the latter is true is it possible to explain the origin of pain as part of the struggle for existence of the species in classical Darwinian terms. Scientists are prone to simplify and ignore the difficulties involved. Although the theory of evolution has many logical weaknesses it still commands most support.

Pradines has made an extremely important contribution to the subject by his critical analysis of the theory. We shall reproduce it here in broad outline.

Intense pain paralyses activity by causing bewilderment and interrupting co-ordination of movement. If this is so, writes Pradines, natural selection could only develop a moderate sense of pain, so that the limits of what is purposeful are not transgressed. The result of evolution, then, must be a moderate sense of pain. But if the degree of intensity of pain felt were limited in this way, the organism would only require to be able to react adequately to stimuli in order to preserve it from all dangers. Sensitivity to a stimulus for pain would be sufficient and it would not require to be accompanied by a sensation of pain. 'It is not true that we can know pain without suffering it, that is to say without being subjected to it twice over.' For pain always comes

95

too late. Pradines thus rejects the theory that pain sensation evolved from sensitivity to stimulus. In its place he suggests that the fully developed skin sense found at a higher stage of development consists in sensitivity to stimulus, which was originally a means of defence with exclusively negative reactions, having developed into a genuine sense of touch with qualitative sensations and formed perceptions. Sensibility to stimuli could well become a perfect instrument for protective reflexes, without actually turning into a pain or touch sense. Animal intelligence could even influence it in such a manner so as to transform it into a sensation, that is, a means of judicious self-defence. The feeling of pain could then be dispensed with. Pain itself could never have been a form, nor a phase, nor indeed the object of differentiation of stimuli, although it might have been the inevitable result of this development. 'Life has encountered it unsought and cannot refuse it without rejecting itself too.'

Pain is not a primary fact in the evolution of the skin senses nor the sense of touch in its final form. On the contrary pain may be said to originate in the sense of touch: 'it produces pain as effect follows cause'. This *had to* happen because the sensitive faculties (i.e. the ability to acquire knowledge by means of the senses) depended for their existence on a higher degree of consciousness. Originally, stimuli aroused unconscious defensive reflexes. They then became painful emotions with the emergence of consciousness along with the ability to acquire knowledge through the senses. 'In penetrating pain consciously the senses also learned to experience its painfulness.' This does not mean, however, that the sensation of pain comes into existence in the course of the evolution of the sense of touch. The nerve endings sensitive to pressure are always separate from the pain points in the skin, as v. Frey has demonstrated.

The tactile sense exercises only an indirect influence on the sensation development of pain. The importance of a sense organ lies in its function and not in the actual organ itself. A good example of what this means is the eye and its functional role for the whole body. 'The visual sense acts like a light for the nerves which guide the muscles.' Although the organs of the sense of touch serve the parts of the body in which they occur, the sense of touch has also highly developed end organs which are at the service of the whole body.

In fact the entire nervous system benefits from the evolution of the skin senses. Their influence extends far beyond forming specific isolated paths and local reflexes. Differentiation can cause the stimulus to become painful once the protective dam of the tactile sense has been pierced. According to Pradines, there is a dual causal relationship between touch perception and pain. As regards the *general* effect, the relationship is *indirect* and distant. Where the tactile sense puts a check on pain, the relationship is local and *direct*. How are we to account for this?

Speaking in a general sense and not with specific regard to man, we can say that intelligence develops at the cost of the emotions. It does not create pain out of sensitivity. 'The achievement of the intelligence lies in its reducing the force of the emotions; its impotence lies in the fact that it creates them at all.' We can thus formulate two laws for the association between the sense of touch and skin pain: (i) a law of indirect sensitivization; (ii) a law of direct suppression.

Pradines proves the first of these by showing that pain is hardly developed among the lower animals and only appears among the higher animals which possess consciousness and intelligence. Their intelligence depends on the degree of clearness of consciousness. The extraordinary degree of increased sensitivity to pain among mammals proves the great importance of the evolution of the touch sense, that is, the *realization* of what *affects* the subject. It is still disputed as to whether domestic horses and dogs are more sensitive to pain than a cart horse or a watch dog, and how far the difference depends on intelligence and sensitivity to touch.

Pradines supposes a positive relationship between the degree of intelligence and sensitivity to touch among human beings and a negative one between these two variables and sensitivity to pain. As demonstrated by various tests, primitive peoples and the mentally deficient are less sensitive to pain. These tests have also established a particularly keen sense of touch among the former.

Our information as regards the human sphere is still very far from complete, but it does indicate that pain is a concomitant of greater intelligence. We can, of course, sense, but not prove, what is meant by greater 'intelligence'. Does it imply the existence of concealed psychic structures, a mental attitude to one's own body? We could show that intelligence is not directly related to sensitivity to pain in the form of ability to think and act, but that it rather represents another mark of human development, often, but not always, accompanied by intelligence (cf. Note 52). We must decide how far it is possible to establish sensitivity to pain. Experimental investigation is not always the most appropriate method for this.

Pradines' concept of the association between intelligence and pain not as 'a natural link which is also constitutionally determined' but as a 'link whose derivation is distant and indirect' proves his deep insight into the nature of the problem. He concludes his remarks on the law of indirect sensitivization with the pithy phrase: 'Pain is the bastard child of shame which the intelligence produced in the stimulus before deserting it.'

His proof of the second law, concerned with the relationship between the sense of touch and the feeling of pain, 'the law of l'inhibition directe', lies in the greater transmission speed of touch impressions as compared with impressions. Goldscheider and others after him have proved that we become conscious of touch impressions before we feel pain. The explanation given by v. Frey was the longer peripheral latency, that is, the stimulus to the pain nerve endings, which is chemical, takes longer than the stimulus to touch points. Nowadays we explain the time lag by the different quality of the nerve conductors. The painful stimulus runs along thin pain fibres at a lower transmission speed than the thicker fibres of the touch impressions. This difference, as already

98

stated, exists for secondary pain only. Primary pain, 'sens de piqûre' (Piéron), appears almost simultaneously with the sense of touch.

Apart from the mechanism responsible for the delayed sensation of pain, Pradines regards the latter as a case of adaptability which is organically purposeful. Agreeing with our view of the connexion between pain and fear, he remarks that pain is a sort of answer to an 'anguished alertness: something in us is set in motion before it actually appears'. Less acceptable is his remark, despite the witty formulation, that pain, a quality of the stimulus, is conducted so slowly because the stimulus is 'slow and heavy in its movements like persons burdened with responsibility. It must decide whether or not there is any pain.' Pain hides itself behind the touch sense, as the king hides behind the pawn and other figures in chess. This is perhaps true of what is known in physiology as secondary pain which is genuine pain, causing suffering. The stimulus, however, which causes defensive reflexes, is conducted very rapidly and becomes conscious as primary pain. It usually passes very quickly and is no more than a sensation of sharpness or a sting making us aware of some external act. As Piéron once remarked, nearly all studies of the subject have overlooked the true problem of pain by concentrating on this primary pain. Pradines' hypothesis is the most astute biological analysis of the connexion between pain and touch sense in existence. It explains at the same time the evolution of pain and its appearance at an advanced stage of development. It requires, however, in my opinion, some emendation. Greater clearness of consciousness and what the French scientist calls 'intelligence'—a concept we will not analyse here, but simply take in the sense of heightened awareness and possession (also self-possession)—are only the *prerequisite* of sensing pain. This can be sensed in two ways, either a sharp impression in the skin, or gnawing, genuine pain, which leaves a deeper impression. We saw that the first was an unconscious stimulus in the case of the lower animals, producing defensive reflexes, while the second was derived from a confluence of impressions in all organs (blood vessels, capsules, periosteum) which regulate the vegetative processes with the aid of the nervous system. The evolution of sensory perception causes *both* types of stimulus to be transmitted to consciousness indirectly. Pain sensation is therefore a given state of awareness of having been injured. It does not primarily belong to the 'vital' functional processes. It cannot be comprehended by the understanding: its purpose is therefore the *secondary* one of judiciously regulating future behaviour.

Henry Head's experiment furnished adequate proof for Pradines' second law of direct inhibition of pain. This experiment formed the basis of numerous neurophysical theories including that of phylogenesis of the sensory functions.

In his own person Head examined the return of skin sensitivity to a severed nerve during the process of healing.[75] The most important result was that pain sense returned before the sense of touch and that there was a period of hyperanalgesia which gradually faded when the touch sense had come back. Despite criticism the result seems to be correct. Head explained it as follows: genetically the sense of pain is the most primitive skin sense: it causes sensations only and not perceptions. This Head termed *protopathic* sensitivity. When a nerve is regenerated, the latter is the first to return. When the sense of touch follows, much later, bringing with it the ability to distinguish objective impressions, this so-called *epicritic* sensitivity represses or *inhibits* the protopathic. It is only then that the pointedness of a sharp needle can be felt independently of the sensation of pain which *follows*. Many scientists have adopted this distinction between protopathic as the more primitive and older, and the epicritic, more recent and differentiated. Head's assumption that the epicritic sense exercises a constricting effect on the protopathic has been used to explain various pathological disturbances in sensitivity.

The epicritic stimuli are rapidly conducted and rise up to the cortex. There they exercise, it is assumed, a constricting influence on pain impressions which follow after a brief interval only as far as the thalamus. Neurologists favouring anatomical interpretations content themselves with this simple explanation, while those who think on more functional lines are aware of the danger of premature definition of complicated relationships by providing a simple explanation of *separate* associations. Anyone acquainted with the literature on touch and pain sense will realize that Head's explanation is a little hasty. Ariëns Kappers,[76] basing his assertions on tests by Boeke and Heringa, suggests that all young unmyelinated nerve fibres are sensitive to pain and that therefore when the majority of fibres are myelinated, the skin's sensitivity to pain diminishes. Boeke and Heringa found that touch corpuscles were in full process of regeneration as early as the hyperalgetic stage. They therefore assume that these, rather than the thinner sensitive fibres in the sympathetic system and their free endings, are responsible for the return of the protopathic feeling. Against all these theories based on anatomy there is the fact that if the bloodstream is sealed off, a state of hyperalgesia emerges.[77] One would expect an examination of the blood supply to yield different reactions from different nerve endings. But v. Weizsäcker's assumption, based on clinical experience, is far more probable, namely that peripheral and central agents cause a functional change in the co-ordination of the skin senses. And so hyperalgesia and hypoaesthesia are sometimes found simultaneously in the aforementioned causalgia, without evidence of any peripheral anatomical change.

Pradines made some very valuable observations on Head's famous test. The significance of this lies, he says, in its having demonstrated how the affective sensation of pain is suppressed by the epicritical 'gnostic' touch sense. But this is by no means its only, nor even its most significant, contribution: still more valuable is the information thereby communicated to the organism on objects with which the organism comes into contact. Although Head realized well enough that 'The aim of human evolution is for the functions of the mind to gain control over the emotions and instincts', yet the development of the former is not promoted by suppressing the protopathic sense, which is an exclusively negative act. There must be a positive evolution as well, and this demands not only a peripheral and central nervous order but also a psychic structure. Intelligence is based on these preconditions and the emotional life determined by them. Pradines is correct in saying: 'The intelligence is not merely a lower affectivity.' The first significant explanation of inhibition of pain is to be found in terms of the psychophysical evolution of animal life *as a whole*.

In asserting that protopathic sensitivity is both natural and primary, Head goes beyond the evidence of his experiment. As Pradines rightly says, the assertion is refuted by reflection on the actual facts themselves. These show that this particular pain sensation only appears at an advanced stage of evolution and is all but lacking in lower animals. The protopathic sense would in any case be an insufficient protection against harmful influences. Head's tests show too that it is characterized by its poor localization. It spreads far beyond the injured area and is latent over a long period. Its after-effects are even more protracted. It is impossible to see how such an apparatus in nature could develop and be of value in the struggle for existence. 'Head's protopathic state could never characterize the *primitive* constitution of a living being.'

In other words we must rather think of a subject who, once having attained a certain degree of consciousness, experiences sufficiently strong physical stimuli as something unpleasant, i.e. as pain; these emotions are constricted, a process of major functional significance. Should functional harmony be upset, either by peripheral causes—as in Head's test or as in causalgia—or by central causes—as when the posterior column or spinal cord (Foerster) or the thalamus is injured—pathological hypersensitivity ensues. This can be termed protopathic but it is not a sensory effect.

Anatomical and functional tests of pain made in the early (embryonic) stages of human development are confusing.

Reflexes can be evoked when the actual sense of touch, or at least the organs necessary to form it, are not yet developed. Such reactions to skin stimuli are hardly localized at all. Almost the entire body reacts and the movements it makes are practically without any form. As Coghill says,[78] the organism still acts as a unit. There is a certain resemblance here to reactions to protopathic stimuli, but we are not justified in assuming the existence of pain sensation in embryos. In any case artificial stimuli of this kind and their effects do not contribute to our knowledge of physiological functions and nothing at all towards indicating their possible phylogenesis. An embryo still in the protective covering of its mother's body has no functional connexion with the outside world and is not capable of adequate responses to stimuli.

Comparative anatomical studies (see Ariëns Kappers' excellent summary) show that among·the lower vertebrates the thin, partially unmyelinated, sensory fibres predominate, while the complex end corpuscles are totally lacking or are very few. There is a tendency to try to support the theory of the primary emergence of the protopathic system by these facts (speaking from a phylogenetic point of view). There is of course no objection to this in so far as it is an *anatomical* differentiation and not applied to the evolution of functions.

Ariëns Kappers has expressed the opinion that the distinction between epicritic and protopathic sensitivity applies equally to skin sensation and the more deep-set sensations as well as to other sensory organs. His assertion is based partially on anatomical evidence. Nerve endings which are sensitive to chemical substances (chemoreceptors) in the case of invertebrates or lower vertebrates are just endings of chiefly unmyelinated fibres in the skin or mucosa. Higher chemical receptors, the organs of taste or smell, are connected with myelinated fibres. A distinction in the manner of reaction corresponds to this anatomical distinction. Response to stimuli in the primitive system is usually negative (flight reactions), according to Kappers, whereas in the higher system the reaction is positive (searching movements). The latter has therefore a 'gnostic' function. There is a similar distinction between protopathic—'vital' and epicritic—gnostic perceptions in the visual sense. The former is limited to the functions of the rods in the periphery of the retina, the latter to the cones in the centre of the retina.

These analogies are of value in proving the primary emergence of flight reactions in an animal. But differentiated searching movements, perceptions of form, co-ordinated and limited movements can also be met with among the lower animals. The distinction between the two types of sensibility contributes as little to understanding how the sensory functions came into existence as it does to clarifying the connexion between pain and the touch sense.

We arrive at the conclusion that the simple fact that a sense of pain exists among higher animals is not to be explained in terms of comparative anatomy or animal behaviour. Pain must have a deeper ground than this: it is to be sought for in animal existence itself. The science of biology should not confine itself to describing regulated processes and establishing the causes of variation. It must also try to show how the various forms and qualities which occur are representatives of basic types and so also the marks of animal existence.

If an animal is able to place itself face to face with objects and its own body in its quality of 'centric positionality', then other phenomena make their appearance which are not confined to the purely functional sphere of self-preservation and preservation of the species. An example of this is playing, already referred to, or pain sensation.

What we have already said will have made it clear that the origin of pain is closely related to its function. In considering these problems, it must be borne in mind that the qualities of an animal must not necessarily be of *primary* functional importance. Such qualities can be acquired *secondarily* in a functional connexion, once they are seen to be useful. The function itself is not dependent on the particular quality. Minute details in the structure of the body, the functions of the organs, and animal behaviour convince us of their primary purposefulness, once we accept the specific manner of life, feeding, and milieu of any given species. We cannot perhaps understand why a class or order or especially the main groups of the animal world are what they are. What is the point of four, six, or eight paws, of segmentation or of breathing by means of lungs, gills, windpipe, or of feathers or hair? These qualities merely indicate certain *potentialities*. In such cases we accept the *structural plan* as a *given fact*: to ask their 'purpose' is senseless. In its struggle for existence one or other characteristic of the bee, its basket on its hind paw, can have been advantageous, but not the possession of six instead of eight paws. The *meaning*, not the purpose, of the basic characteristics of plants and animals can only be grasped as part of a hierarchical order in the natural world and of the irreducible laws of its evolution. Few attempts indeed have been made to analyse the logic of such an interpretation.

The most general animal characteristics are its compact form, its *gestaltet* relation to its environment, division into two sexes, the feelings, ability to learn, striving towards an object, and expressive movements. These can only be meaningful if seen as part of the 'idea' of animal being and the metaphysical conception of a fundamental bond linking human being and nature. Here—independent of all evolutionary hypotheses—we discover a scheme, a suggestion, in lower nature a 'shadow' whose full significance is only revealed in man. Significance implies far more here than mere purposefulness (that is, purposeful relationship between means and achievement).

Feelings and expressive movements are not primarily purposeful, although they can in fact be adopted in a functional context, *secondarily*, once they are already in existence. This is clear in the case of pain. Flight movements can emerge without pain being felt, without even the stimulus being painful.

The sensation of weariness, as Scheler says,[79] utters something that in the language of mind is equivalent to 'rest!', dizziness at the edge of an abyss: 'step back!', while appetite or disinclination to eat gives us emotional information as to the advantage or harmfulness of food. Pain only communicates the actual *state* of affliction. If the existence of feelings is accepted as a fact which cannot be explained from nature, only some feelings can be said to possess functional powers. With regard to the relationship between pain and the formation of habit among animals we come to the conclusion that it could not be explained teleologically. Violent pains upset habit formation and indeed all ordered movement, as we have already seen.

Von Uexküll's interpretation of what is purposeful provides an example of the weird structures called forth by the riddle of pain. According to this biologist, pain serves to prevent self-mutilation. 'Therefore pain interrupts and inhibits an act in progress which might cause harm to the body.' This, he says, is particularly necessary among carnivorous animals. Rats devour their own paws if the sensory nerves are severed. Insects have no pain sense for many of them sacrifice their limbs when in danger in order to preserve their bodies. The constricting effect of pain would be bound to upset the reflexes 'and can therefore be regarded as non existent'. If one pushes the hind part of a dragon-fly's body between its jaws, it will begin to devour its own body. Uexküll, however, overlooks the fact that an insect will never devour its own paw, despite its lack of pain sensation, not even in cleaning it with its jaws. 'Most lower animals are built in such a manner that they can never be in danger of harming their own bodies.' His conclusion that pain is to be found 'wherever it has a share in the plan of the organism and is accordingly necessary and useful' is completely without foundation.[80]

IV

Pain and Experience

(i) FEELING OR SENSATION

*'All pain, then, must consist in an effort,
an effort that is ineffective.'* BERGSON[81]

HUMAN life is alone in being able to understand the nature
of pain. Only human beings can make their experience
of pain the subject of reflection. It may be subjected to
examination as it appears in various circumstances, as it grows
and acquires a certain structure, and it may be analysed under
various aspects. The manifold associations of pain with other
objects of consciousness and qualities of the personality are only
to be grasped fully in human beings.

Such analysis belongs to the field of psychology which
requires, in addition to its own study of life phenomena, an ontological interpretation of human existence. This is supplied by
philosophical anthropology, which facilitates the system of co-
ordination necessary for a fuller understanding of the life of the
soul.

The separation of philosophical anthropology from biology
which has come to be accepted in the course of the evolution of
psychology as a science is, however, maintained in experimental
investigation of 'objects of consciousness'. Thus the approach to
the psychology of pain is predetermined along certain lines. To
judge from modern textbooks, works of reference, or from

publications in modern journals, the psychology of pain is merely concerned with a series of facts belonging to sense physiology, facts which emerge from experiments on the relationship of stimulus and effect in varying circumstances. Thus the revision by H. Greehle and F. Dorsch of Th. Elsenhans' *Lehrbuch der Psychologie*, published in 1939,[82] contains a short and quite incomplete summary of observations and experiments already dealt with in the section on the physiology of pain. In the course of the fairly substantial chapter on 'The Feelings', pain is not even mentioned. Other textbooks do not differ greatly in this respect. Obviously the strong positivistic tendencies in psychology which demand the exclusion of philosophy from science and emphasize the merits of the experimental method have caused the problems to dwindle in importance. It is typical of this outlook that the chapter in Sauerbruch and Wenke's work *Wesen und Bedeutung des Schmerzes*[83] (1936) entitled 'Psychologische Voraussetzungen' quotes literature exclusively from the generation of twenty-five years previously.

Whereas the very methods of modern psychology are an obstacle to the analysis of pain, psychiatry accepts the unity of human existence with its roots in the 'vital' sphere. It therefore maintains the tradition of older philosophers and psychologists. In the works of men like O. Schwarz, Bilz, v. Weizsäcker, v. Gebsattel, Straus, and others, the predominant problems are psychophysical in nature: pain is considered in relation to problems of general biology, to the study of the emotions and the will, to the voluntary motor system, to conditions of life, and to the personality. It goes without saying that interest is still shown in the sort of questions discussed by leading psychologists of the earlier generation, Wundt, Stumpf, v. Kries, Külpe, Titchener, Ziehen, Becher:[84] does pain belong to the sensations or to the feelings?

The question of classification is not unimportant. It serves as a useful guide in investigating the essential characteristics of the sensory impressions and of the feelings. Wenke was right to reassess the question: sensation or feeling? If we are to understand the feeling of pain, he says, we must bear in mind that sensation takes place in a neutral sphere of consciousness, while feeling is directly related to our personal outlook. Furthermore it forces us to take arbitrary decisions. Pain has the characteristics of a sensation, i.e. it has its origin in a stimulus and the impression cannot be reduced nor analysed. Pain also has the character of a feeling, e.g. its deep effects. Therefore Wenke and many other psychiatrists agree with older psychologists in asserting that pain is both sensation and feeling. What actually is the connexion between the two?

The most obvious solution would seem to be a process of mutual absorption. Psychologists, however, try to distinguish as clearly as possible between the various species of objects of consciousness and psychic processes. And so the connexion between the two in the experience of pain had to be defined more explicitly. This is the point of the discussion.

Psychologists with pronounced leanings towards physiology, such as Ziehen and Titchener, took as their starting point the sensations, the immediate outcome of sense stimuli. They considered that all objects of consciousness originate from sensory material. All very strong sense impressions acquire—in Ziehen's opinion—an emotional tone which, in the case of pain, is *displeasure*; they also have the characteristics common to all sensations, quality and intensity. This emotional tone can become so strong that the quality of the original sensation, pressure, warmth, etc., is obliterated.

Külpe pointed out, in reply, that desire and distaste themselves possess quality and intensity and are therefore analogous to sensations: they are not the 'emotional tone' of another sensation. Furthermore, the relationship between the sensation and the feeling of pain can certainly not be explained by a simple scheme of intensity of sensation and intensity of distaste. The facts disprove such a suggestion. Although the painful stimulus remains constant, the displeasure can vary largely in degree and character:

pain can even be accompanied by feelings of desire without any displeasure.

It is characteristic of the incipient stages of development of science to try to settle the problems of conceptual definition before turning to factual and theoretical knowledge. This was true in the case of the psychologists who overlooked an important methodological principle: the *selection* of those concepts fundamental for their discipline already implies certain interpretation of experience. Thus the idea of the sensations as an independent category is the result of experimental method trying to achieve a constant result by isolating and stabilizing the conditions of the test. In this sense, the separation of, or at least the distinction between, sensations, feelings, conceptions, thoughts, and decisions was accepted and an attempt was made to explain experience in terms of these basic concepts.

In the case of pain this attempt was unsuccessful. Stumpf therefore defined pain as a 'sensation of feeling' and defended his interpretation against his leading contemporaries. A single incident in this conflict throws light on the whole issue. In his 'Apologie der Gefühlsempfindungen'[84] Stumpf attacked Titchener, among others. The latter had rejected Stumpf's thesis that pain is a particular group of sensations, giving rise to a feeling; since, as he said, besides possessing the attributes of quality and intensity, the sensations also possess the quality of clearness. The last mentioned depended on awareness. Feelings do not have this attribute. We cannot draw attention to them; therefore they are not sensations.

Stumpf, in reply, emphasized the division of sensations into species which diverge from one another in more than one respect. Thus sensations of sound are not extended in space, while visual sensations are. Secondly, Stumpf questioned the assertion that clearness is an *attribute* of sensations comparable to other attributes. As for the assertion that it is impossible to draw attention to a feeling, it is necessary, he stated, to distinguish between emotion on the one hand and 'sensations of feeling' on the other.

The emotions do in fact become less potent if notice is taken of them: in the case of sensations this is not so. It is quite possible to draw attention to pain. To do so merely intensifies its character as a feeling. Stumpf therefore reaches the conclusion that 'sense feelings do possess the attribute of clearness and are therefore genuine sensations and not emotions'.

In subscribing to Stumpf's conclusions, we must point out that the actual question 'what is the true relationship between sensation and feeling?' remains unanswered. Nor can we overlook the fact that the point of departure itself is questionable: that sensations are *natural* elements in our consciousness. The older school of psychologists concentrated on laboratory tests and was exclusively concerned with painful impressions in the skin, stings, strong pressure, and heat pain, all of which are more or less sensory in character.

Almost simultaneously with Stumpf's 'Apologie', appeared an essay on 'Gefühlsbegriff und Lust- und Unlustelemente', by E. Becher.[84] Besides giving a general theory of emotional life, the essay includes a definition of pain. A convincing case is made for the view that desire and displeasure are not the product of mutual absorption of sensations but are objects of consciousness which must be clearly distinguished from sensations. He therefore rejects the concept of pain as a sensation of displeasure. Pure pain sensation differs from the latter (which *can* accompany it), just as the quality of bitterness in a taste is different from the unpleasant feeling associated with it. Several types of pain may be distinguished according to qualities peculiar to them, quite apart from the displeasure accompanying the painful impression: thus a pricking sensation in the skin is something quite different from any sort of displeasure, as may be proved if we pinch a fold on the surface of the skin. Sensory displeasure, actual pain, derives from a sensation of pain, according to Becher, and is thus not *itself* a sensation. What is painful or unpleasant in pain is a basic element of consciousness, differing from any other feature of pain in its greater 'life warmth', in its 'not being indifferent'. The importance of this conclusion is that it explains the function of pain in the life of the will and in the biological self-preservation of the individual.

Attempts to define pain psychologically are closely allied to the theory of emotional life. The difficulty in deciding what pain is, sensation or feeling, or a combination of both, or a sensation of feeling, or a sensation followed by a feeling, is a continual reminder of our lack of an adequate theory of feeling. As far back as forty-five years ago Becher wrote: 'The psychology of feeling, despite the efforts of eminent psychologists, is in a state of chaos.' Even today, although we have a theory of feeling advanced by Krüger,[85] among others, as well as other theories, we have no real theory at our disposal to explain the characteristics, distinctions, evolution, and effects of feelings. The life of the feelings remains 'the whale among the fishes', as Meyer said in 1939.

'The whale has a two-fold distinction among the fishes: first, when seen from a distance, it looms large among them and, secondly, on close examination it is found to be no fish at all. Something like that I predict for the theory of emotions, among the theories in psychological textbooks and periodicals.'[86]

As we have already said, it was the psychiatrists in particular who continued to adhere to the classical problem of the relationship between sensation and emotion. Psychopathologists have shown that emotional disturbances associated with mental disease makes it possible to gain insight into the structure and relationships of experience. A theory of emotions such as psychology is unable to offer is needed for such insight. In his book *Der Formalismus in der Ethik und die materiale Wertethik* the philosopher Max Scheler[87] was the first to provide psychiatrists like K. Schneider, Rümke, P. Schilder, and others with the basis for their own valuable work. Equally important is Scheler's distinction between (*a*) sensory feelings (Stumpf's feeling-sensations), (*b*) physical feelings (as states) and life feelings (as functions), (*c*) purely physical feelings (feelings of self), and (*d*) mental feelings (feelings of personality). Pain belongs to the first group.

All feelings are experienced as being either pleasant or unpleasant, but only sensations of feelings are localized (K. Schneider).[88] This is also true of pain although its localization can often be very indefinite. A second characteristic of sensory feelings mentioned by Scheler is that they constitute a 'state'. Pain proves to us that it is 'necessarily given as a state and never as a function or an act'. We *experience* pain but can only avoid or get rid of its cause. Therefore, as Husserl[89] has said, following Brentano, we must distinguish between *pain sensations* and *suffering from pain*.

Suffering is an intentional act and therefore *refers to the person*, while the sensation of pain can continue independently of the acts which it causes. *Sensory feeling also refers to self*, as Scheler says, yet 'without any relation to a person'. Pain is exclusively a state of mind and therefore cannot be recalled. Nor can it be anticipated. It is impossible to re-feel or to recapitulate or imagine the feeling as it is going to be. 'Sympathos', in its literal sense, is therefore impossible to achieve.

Scheler's astute distinctions and his discovery of certain characteristics have introduced valuable order into apparent chaos. Yet despite this and despite the fruitfulness of his idea of 'levels' of feelings, his definition of pain as a sensation of feeling or a sensory feeling is not quite satisfactory in two respects. In itself, his distinction is correct as also his distinguishing superficial and deep feelings is valid. A deep feeling involves our personal existence, not merely subjectively, in so far as we are aware of our own existence as a personality either emotionally or conceptually, but also objectively, in as much as we are actually *in existence* as persons. A deep feeling is less transitory, which means that it does not pass so quickly and cannot be pushed aside.

Furthermore it actually becomes a positive element in the structure of the personality: it contributes to the formation of character.

The definition of pain as a sensation of feeling, as a sensory feeling, gravely underestimates its deeper effects and this would speak against its validity. Such a definition limits its application to the so-called 'body-self', excluding the lower levels of personality. The definition only takes account of short-lived and non-violent pain. The more violent a pain, the deeper it penetrates, affecting not merely the 'body-self', but our actual personality as well. There is a certain force in the attack. We are not indifferent to it. It is not merely a state. Pain throws us back on ourselves: we actually 'feel' feeling.

If, to follow Husserl, our personal relationship to pain is suffering and the latter an intentional act, then it is in the nature of all forms of genuine pain that they can become a cause of suffering. There is something in pain itself which must challenge the person in the form of a primary emotional sensation. Natorp[90] was, I believe, the first to recognize this in his book *Allgemeine Psychologie*. What he attributes to every kind of sensation is particularly true of pain, namely that it 'includes the original impulse in its concept from the beginning'.

The definition of pain as an emotional sensation is unsatisfactory as it places too little emphasis on the relationship to the centre of the person and does not pay sufficient attention to the *dynamic* factor in pain. We referred to this in our remarks on the relationship between pain and motion. We shall now discuss it more fully.

All sensory impressions, and in particular those with a specifically emotional tone, like an agreeable colour, a harsh sound, or a repellent taste, are all much more directly connected with the motor system than we generally believe. Our experience of them is far more than mere acceptance of quality and intensity; it is an experience of *being moved* and differs according to the sensation. This becomes obvious in the case of pain. The inner motion and the visible reaction which follows it are a constitutive element of the quality and intensity of pain itself. They follow as a matter of course, like the sensory impression itself. Sensation and movement are a unity: there is not just a passive sensation, followed by activity, that is, a reaction. E. Straus, v. Weizsäcker, Minkowski,[91] and others have already acknowledged this fact. Our own experiences in animal psychology point in the same direction.

What Stern,[92] following Gronart, established for feelings applies in particular to pain: namely that man experiences his own state in every feeling as one of striving. Not only does he experience the nature and the direction of his efforts but also himself striving. A man in pain is forced to do something when he is in pain. He is set in motion, so to speak, though not necessarily in a visible manner. When the organism experiences pain, it is active, not passive. Achelis[93] also points out this centrifugal element in pain: 'Pain, then, is experiencing a *performance* of the organism; it is not a sensation.'

What is meant here by 'performance'? Certainly not the matter-of-course reaction to pain in the 'vital' sphere, which in man is associated with active imagination, thinking, and acting in the medium of free spontaneity. What Achelis means is probably identical with what we termed the dynamic factor in pain impressions.

It is interesting that Bergson, in his masterly *Matière et Mémoire*, regards the *'tendance motrice'* as the essential characteristic of pain. Let us examine his approach more closely. In Bergson's opinion experience teaches without any doubt that when a sensation is increased it becomes a feeling, an affect. 'And so the contact with the pin is succeeded by the prick without our realizing the transition. Inversely, as pain decreases its cause is perceived: by representing it to ourselves we make it external, as it were. The difference between affect and perception would therefore seem to be one of degree, not of nature.' In reality emotion and sensation are totally different. Although an increased stimulus causes sensation and perception to disappear and turn into feeling, which is no longer referred to an object, the striking thing about it is the *suddenness* of the change.

Bergson provides us with an explanation of this sudden change, which is also intended to explain the significance of pain. In a single animal cell, as in an amoeba, the sensory and kin-aesthetic nerves are not yet separated and every activity is the direct result of local stimulation. The higher animals, on the other hand, have sensitive nerves, which guard the body like *sentinelles avancées* and which regulate activity. The sensitive elements are condemned to inactivity by the distribution of functions round the body, but they are still sensitive to injury. 'And so pain appears, being in our opinion no more than an effort of the injured part to restore order—a sort of dynamic tendency of a sensitive nerve.'

The idea is a fascinating one, although on close examination it proves to be unclear, since his terms are derived from hetero-geneous spheres of life. The injured part, the sensitive nerve, are anatomical features, 'effort' and 'tendency' refer to the integral behaviour of the whole organism. We cannot therefore speak of an 'effort of the part' unless we are prepared to attribute an independent existence to this 'part'.

It is simpler—and sufficient—to draw attention to the lack of *adequate* local reaction in the case of a stronger stimulus—for example—to the skin. This, however, merely confirms the fact that pain only appears as a result of lesion to the cells of the body, or, to put it differently, when sensitive fibres are pathologically stimulated. We subscribed to this theory—with qualifications—in the section on the physiology of pain. For it is not true to say that extreme stimulation of *all* sensitive fibres produces pain. There is a certain system of fibres—normally inserted into the regulation of vegetative processes—which causes pain if the stimulus is strong. In addition there is the sensitivity to stings and burns in the skin, the point of departure of Bergson's remarks.

There is undoubtedly an element of truth in the notion of

local reaction. A needle which has been swallowed *can* pass through the intestines without causing injury if the mucous membrane reacts in an *adequate* manner to the local sharp stimulations. It must react by contracting the smooth muscle tissue *locally*. The latter moves the mucous membrane in order to enable it to avoid the sharp point of the needle. Thus, quite apart from the question of pain sensitivity of the inner organs, as yet insufficiently analysed, a divergency exists between the skin and the mucous membrane of the intestines. The skin cannot avoid injury to a fixed point, but the wall of the intestines can, at any rate to a certain degree. The distinction lies in the basic difference between the vegetative and animal systems and their functions. A particle of skin is just as incapable of acting independently as any other part of the animal system (a muscle or a sense organ). The nature of the animal system, that is, the system responsible for regulating the relationship between animal and environment, is expressed by the *integration* of the functions. This is attested by the indissoluble unity of perception and action. There is no 'local effort' in Bergson's sense; his statement cannot be taken literally: 'All pain is a local effort and it is this isolation of the effort which causes its ineffectivity, since the organism, by reason of the solidarity of its parts, only reacts to the efforts of the whole.' If we substitute for 'a local effort' the phrase 'an ineffective local reaction' we gain valuable insight. We can then understand how pain comes into existence when the organism tries to do something that it is incapable of doing. Not only is v. Weizsäcker's phrase an apt one: 'What we neglect to do is painful,' we must also say: 'What we do wrong is what causes something to hurt.' Since in a sense all our activity is 'wrong'—by reason of the very imperfection of our organization, whose activity is always applied to a *limited* section of reality in space and time—it is true in an even deeper sense that *every activity is the source of suffering*.

This view approximates to the Buddhist doctrine of suffering and the technique of overcoming it. Seen from this angle we can accept as valid Bergson's view that 'All pain must then consist in an effort, an effort that is ineffective.' These words betray deeper insight than Achelis's statement that 'pain is experiencing a performance of the organism'. Pain does not consist in experiencing activity. *Powerless* effort is painful and it imparts to physical injury its painfulness, its 'pathological' character. We have already indicated the soothing effects of inactivity and relaxation and how the empathic character of pain depends on our own personal attitude to our body.

Let us pursue Bergson's train of thought still further. He makes three other important assertions: (i) that pain is a local 'effort' which is out of proportion to the danger threatening the organism; (ii) that the sensation must suddenly turn into an emotional impression and the sensation of pain appear suddenly. 'This is when the disinterested portion of the organism, instead of assimilating the stimulus, repulses it'; and (iii) that the difference between perceptions and affections is one of essence, not of degree.

The discrepancy between pain and the extent of the injury or the seriousness of the danger is striking. We come across innumerable examples of this in clinics. A slight bruise causes greater pain than a deep cut with a sharp object such as a knife or glass. This discrepancy forces us to rely on experience in judging the symptomatic importance of pain. Experience, not the intensity of pain, determines medical diagnosis, for certain types of pain are associated with certain types of illness and they follow a similar course. A doctor's interest in the smallest pain and the nuances in its quality proves the discrepancy between the intensity of the pain and actual danger. It proves too that pain is not a sensation and has no primary biological or physiological function.

With reference to Bergson's assumption of a *sudden* transformation of the sensations—pressure, heat, etc.—into pain, we can say as follows: if a line 'g' represents the difference in intensity between the weakest barely perceptible touch impression on a point on the skin and the strongest, not yet painful one, and a line 'p' the distance between the weakest and the strongest painful impression, then the lines 'g' and 'p' do not converge at a point: they actually cover each other for a stretch 'o', which in comparison with their total length is very small indeed. This can be demonstrated by experiment: the length of 'g', 'p', and 'o' is not equal for all parts of the skin. 'G' is long at a touch point, 'p' at a pain point, while on the horny skin 'g' is extremely small. We have no experimental data on the length of the transition zone 'o'. We have the impression that 'o' is small in relation to 'g' and 'p', that is, on not too exact observation the transition is very sudden. Occasionally, as when, for example, pressure is applied over a large surface, pressure and pain are felt simultaneously; 'o' is then fairly long. Sometimes in such cases a pain sensation appears *alongside* the pressure. At first slight and inconsistent, it can be clearly distinguished from the pressure. There is an initial stage in headaches, toothaches, or inner pains when the actual sensation of pain is uncertain, where a person says 'I think I am getting a pain' or 'there is a pain coming but it isn't there yet'.

In such cases the feeling of 'being subject' to something, gnawing, drilling, burning, pinching, can be present without its actually hurting. If the intensity increases gradually, then the stretch 'o' where 'g' and 'p' coincide is fairly long, but the moment of the appearance of pain can be indicated more or less clearly. *For in addition to the gnawing which can be objectivated, pain appears as a physical emotion.*

When an impression of pain is felt on the skin there is a reaction, a sort of reversal of innervation, besides the sense of having been touched. Not the subject itself, but *la portion intéressée*, tries to get rid of the stimulus. What Bergson calls 'assimilate' and 'repulse' is not to be understood in terms of actual motion but in the sense of two forms of intentional attitude. The first is an activity which can be and is executed, which possesses a certain aim and is purposeful, forming the basis of sensory knowledge.

The second is an 'ineffective effort' which cannot be put into action; it becomes a representative expressive movement and leads to experiencing resistance, actually suffering pressure or a sting, etc., in or on a part of the body. Purposeful activity following an impression, whether action or perception (sensory recognition), is fundamentally different from a *helpless* state of being *forced* to endure something. These essentially distinctive attitudes *cannot* merge and they are at the root of the sudden transfer from sensation (and perception) to the feeling of pain, the affection.

The correctness of Bergson's third assertion follows from this, that the difference between 'perception' and 'affection' is one of essence, not of degree.

No modern thinker has shown such fundamental opposition to the academic psychologists and their methods as Ludwig Klages[94] in his criticism of their basic principles and their methods. Like Bergson he regards sensation and feeling as essentially different processes. Sensation is experiencing resistance, intensity, pressure, and counter-pressure. Klages is even more logical in his emphasis on the unity between sensation and self-movement than v. Weizsäcker. Qualities and forms are experienced by beholding: this gives the content of the sensation space, position, and individuality. We perceive images of the world by means of the senses' ability to behold. 'Sensing' is always 'finding'; in the German word *'Empfinden'*, 'emp' means 'anti' (originally in Greek 'against' in space) and corresponds to the English 'answer' and German *'Antwort'*. Feeling, on the other hand, is not localized in a particular place (in the body or the external world). It is 'metaphysically' present in the psyche, the opposite pole of the body. 'No psychic process exists of which feeling does not form a part, and no feeling which is not the feeling of an individual psyche.' Sensation and feeling are so distinct from each other that Klages refuses to accept the phrase 'sensation of feeling'.

The thesis is, broadly speaking, acceptable but pain proves that sensation as a localized experience of sensing resistance and intensity is *at the same time* a genuine feeling (in Klages' sense) of danger, a feeling of being afflicted in a painful manner; a feeling that the threat and the injury are connected with the sensation of stinging, burning, gnawing, tearing, etc. Stumpf's definition of pain as primarily a sensation remains the correct one, and 'sensation of feeling' is only valid in so far as a sensation is understood in the sense of a *'tendance motrice'* contained *in* the pain itself and simultaneously affecting us as a feeling.

Klages' criticism is not alone directed against the commonly held theory of sensation, he also offers a theory of feeling which we shall examine more closely in connexion with the problem of pain. Feelings, like moods, are also 'impulsive experiences'. All feelings differ in quality and intensity, but they cannot be classified according to pleasure and displeasure. The so-called pleasurable feelings are feelings of success, the displeasurable of failure. Klages considers that the reason for the usual distinction of feelings on the basis of pleasure and displeasure arises from a mistaken identification of life with spirit going back over two thousand years. The so-called life processes are confused with the activity of the will, psyche with self. Attention has therefore been concentrated on the significance of feeling for human consciousness instead of referring it to the numerous qualities and expressive character of emotional life.

Klages' concept contains an element of truth and one relevant to the psychology of pain. Violent *displeasure* in pain is actually the expression of helplessness which comes home to man in suffering. Displeasure is to be distinguished from painfulness, since, as in the case of an animal, it is the experience of a qualitative, more precisely an oppressive, mood and the desire to escape from it. To the inclination towards flight which follows a painful stimulus is added the *inability* to escape from pain. This, then, is the peculiar character of pain: to burn, gnaw, and oppress the body in various ways so that its adequate expression is a scream, in fact 'an ineffective effort'.

(ii) THE ACT OF BEING HURT
AND THE STATE OF BEING HURT

*'If sensation is communication between self
and the world, every sensation affects self
in some manner.'* E. STRAUS.[95]

The quality of an emotion is a given, non-reducible fact about which nothing can be said. Red is red and pain is pain. To see red, on the other hand, is a fact which can be analysed further: an example is Goethe's theory of colours. The same is true of feeling pain in the way man feels it. In other words, a painful impression is an extreme abstraction, while the feeling of pain is a real, concrete event, possessing structure and essence and—possibly—significance.

Sensations are not factors occurring in the normal course of life, in the sense that the sense organs provide men and animals with no quantitative or qualitative *static* impressions. The sense organs are the means of establishing relations with the outside world. Being sensible of something is subjective; it means being involved in a situation. Seen as a *dynamic* relation it possesses the full value of a life function in contrast to 'the' individual sensation. 'There are no such things as sensations in themselves, there are only sensitive beings,' as Straus wrote in his book *Vom Sinn der Sinne*. The nature and significance of pain are only to be understood by conceptual analysis of the concrete phenomenon of 'a man in pain'. This is not to be reached by so-called introspection based 'on the belief that true sensations are independent of subjective attitudes and depend only upon local stimulation as purely local experiences' (Köhler).[96] This knowledge must be related to the idea of man, to absolute being in metaphysical terms, before we can formulate a *theory* of pain.

The variations on the image of man in pain can be reduced

to *two* basic types: the *injured* and the *suffering*. The first is demonstrated by a man screaming, grimacing, retracting a bodily extremity, or reaching for the injured part if it is on his head or torso. A suffering person acts in quite a different manner. He sighs, groans, and laments. He twists and turns and moves his head one way or another, his fists and teeth clenched, and his eyes are closed in pain or fixed in an empty stare.

What do these two images tell us? The first indicates an act, the second a state. Where someone has been or is being afflicted at a particular moment, the expressions within the two categories are related in a remarkable way.

Let us examine the first case a little more closely. A person can be afflicted in every possible way, by all kinds of agents, and in all conceivable circumstances. Yet in the actual process of being struck or touched there is always a more or less explosive reaction, for example a cry, varying according to the nature of the affliction—injury or astonishment, fear, pain, fright, pity, etc. A study of spontaneous verbal utterances in such cases among different peoples, children, and animals would be very rewarding. An exclamation of sudden pain contains an element of astonishment. At the same time it is a convulsive start as if in fright, followed by what we so significantly term a *paralysing* sensation.

Fear and sudden fright are accompanied, as far as I can see, by a marked reversal of innervation. This is understandable since the expressive movement in both cases represents an inversion, in this case, of course, retreat and flight. The reversal of innervation is the most general form of such reaction, withdrawal or flight is merely one particular case of it. On this basis we find purposeful and sometimes purposeless movements following pain and fright.

A person standing collapses, a person sitting jumps up. Hanging arms are drawn together, or even raised. An open hand closes and grips something; the rima glotis, which is usually relaxed, tenses, while the sphincter muscles slacken: the jaw sags. Exhalation or inhalation is pronounced, according to the phase of breathing at the moment of attack. The vowels a, o, i can be heard in the exclamation: they have a toneless, blowing sound, often the character of a double note. Contraction predominates in the case of pain, paralysis in fright. Both are present in the case of sudden injury, fright, and pain: thus the sounds: aiii . . . or auuu.[97]

Sudden pain comes under the category of the act of being afflicted: it is an unexpected rupture of communication between organism and milieu. Although the phenomenon of being afflicted has the character of a rupture, of union destroyed, the converse is not true. Not every rupture is an affliction in the above sense. Such a situation only occurs when there is something there which *continues* in existence after the affliction has taken place, something which is *itself* afflicted *and yet not*. Thus although there are all sorts of similar phenomena and we speak of a house or tree being stuck by lightning, strictly speaking it is only correct where something is subjected to attack, is afflicted and yet remains itself. Obviously only an animal existence, an individual, can fulfil such requirements and this only if individualization is sufficiently pronounced so as to be capable of responding with a genuine attitude to everything around, inside and on the individual. In other words, only among men—and to a certain extent among higher animals—is this possible. An organism which can be afflicted, that is, which can experience injury to itself, is the only type which can be frightened and made to suffer pain. An insect cannot be frightened and does not feel pain.

Before considering the painful nature of affliction, that is, of being hurt, as against other kinds of affliction, we may assume on the basis of the phenomena as such that fright and sudden sensations of pain appear together as ways of being afflicted. In another sense, however, the two are mutually exclusive. Experience, in fact, reveals that this is so. Fear obliterates pain. A doctor who makes his patient look away during an operation is prompted by this same experience. The patient gets such a fright at the sudden incision that the sensation of pain is obviated or at least reduced.

Or a door can be slammed or some other 'overwhelming' impression created.

Although painful affliction always involves some degree of fright, injury (to any point in the body) differs from all other types of affliction. Anyone afflicted by something in the external world stands transfixed before the agent. The hand or foot, or whatever it is, is in the forefront of the experience, although the painful emotion at a centre point of one's own body strikes at the very centre of one's own existence, one's 'self'. This is true in a peculiar sense. A fright means that a person has been affected by *something*, which, no matter how overwhelming, is and still remains outside him, so to speak. Despite all *resonance of feeling* and emotional *reaction*, it confronts him and cannot claim his *whole* psychophysical person. Pain, on the other hand, attacks man *in* his psychophysical unity: he no longer experiences something confronting him, but *in* himself.

Three conclusions can be drawn from this: First, such affliction is far more *direct*, one might say *unavoidable*: man seems irrevocably abandoned. Second, the disturbance of physical integrity destroys the structural connexion of the sensory motor system. In *painful* affliction, dynamic moments seem to predominate, tension relaxes, and so movements ensue; in fright, static moments are primary, the motor system becomes quite rigid. In the case of a weak peripheral impression, the dynamic moment expresses itself in flight movement simply by withdrawing hand or foot. If pain is violent, all sorts of chaotic movements ensue. Retracting or withdrawing an extremity is not just a purposeful act, it is *also* an expressive movement. Part of the body is brought back again, so to speak, into one's own circle, back into the protected area: it is 'rescued'. If it is not possible to withdraw the hurt part, then we lay our hand on it; this is *almost* as inevitable as flight reaction.

Since retreat is primarily a reflex and consequently precedes pain among animals also, even those without a cerebrum, its expressive character is therefore only secondary. To lay one's hand on one's breast or stomach, to grasp an injured part of the body, is a direct *personal* reaction: the injury is experienced pathologically and the expressive movement demonstrates this.

A third result of the attack on man *in* his psychophysical unity by pain (and not attack on psychophysical unity as such) is that the emphasis is laid on the self-conscious which is much more an element of pain than of fear. If someone wants to know whether he is awake or dreaming, he pinches himself. No other sensation demonstrates as clearly that he 'is there'.

Philosophers and psychologists have demonstrated this in various forms, namely that consciousness, and especially the self-conscious, develops in and by means of painful impressions. But we must distinguish between the development of physical consciousness, the feeling of self, and the actual self-conscious, where the subject is aware of itself as an independent undivided unit face to face with the world. According to Preyer a child must make many experiments with the parts of its own body, which it can feel and see, before being able to recognize it as its own. These experiences are for the most part painful ones. 'Pain brings the child to knowledge of itself.'[98]

Consciousness of oneself as knowledge of personal being is *not* merely the result of painful experiences but also of the manner in which these (and other) experiences in excentric position are actually experienced as one's own. In the first year the child acquires a body sense (Ch. Bühler[99]) whereas it is not until the middle of the second that it gains selfconsciousness, as is shown by the fact that it no longer refers to itself in the third person. It has a feeling of self. It is able to differentiate between the concepts 'me' and 'you'. Painful impressions do not rouse the self-conscious in this sense. An animal will never arrive at a self-conscious despite many painful impressions. For an animal is unable to refer these as its own experiences to their existential ground. An animal can undoubtedly experience affliction, but not in its *own* psychophysical unity. If this is true of a spirit, then the consciousness of self and the external world certainly becomes increasingly clear through all forms of 'enduring'. Nicolai Hartmann[100] writes: 'If I am struck or pushed, I am directly informed beyond all argument of the reality of whatever strikes or pushes me.' It is not necessary to know the cause, as some theorists assert, in order to be able to gain an image of reality. 'This image, or more correctly, the certainty of the reality of what is pushing or striking is given in endurance just as directly as the fact of pain itself.' We experience pain—and I emphasize this— just as directly as we experience reality, but we know it is quite different, our experience takes the form of an act of being afflicted.

Pain, like all forms of suffering, forces man to reflect: we have already referred to this. But the reality of the external world and our personal existence can never be established by painful impressions alone. Scheler's observation in a footnote to his anthropological sketch[101] cannot be accepted as such. 'All consciousness is grounded in *suffering* and all higher stages of consciousness in *intensified* suffering.'

If painful affliction exceeds a maximum degree of intensity the result is either loss of consciousness or the state of painlessness known as *trauma*. This phenomenon was discovered a long time ago. We meet it in writings of antiquity where it is related that men suffered grievous injuries and even martyrdom without so much as a cry of pain. There are similar accounts from later ages of war injuries or torture. Furthermore there are cases of amputations and major operations being performed without narcotics and yet without pain being felt. In our own time we know of injuries received in war which elicited no reaction.

If we take all these facts and assess them, we are left with two general situations where trauma occurs. One is in a state of extreme exhaustion, mental depression, fright, horror, when we are overcome with dread; the second is given with a state of intense mental activity, ecstasy, or absorption by an overruling emotional image, complete dedication to some sublime task.

To explain trauma in terms of distraction of attention would be incorrect. It would be false even in the simplest case of insensitivity to pain in battle or a state of rage or fear. A soldier sees and hears well, he feels the pressure of the bullet, the cut of the sabre, but not the pain inflicted. In rage or fear the sense organs cover a wide field and perceive with great accuracy every aspect of the situation which is causing the emotion. 'Blindness' and 'deafness' only apply to those things where contact is severed through an emotional situation. The selective function of the sense organs is general among animals: among humans it is exceptional and occurs only in cases such as these. An animal only notices what *concerns* itself, what is biologically important, instigating activity and regulating it. In fighting too it is insensitive to pain.

The explanation of trauma lies in the fact that painful affliction of a subject is interwoven with the experience that it is *he* (and no other) who is afflicted. The subject must therefore be 'in possession of himself'. This is not true of violent emotions nor of an animal, although despite its lack of reflexive self-conscious an animal can be 'in possession of itself' inasmuch as it can be 'in possession' of anything, its food, or its young. An animal can be afflicted in its young and equally so in its own body. The latter it experiences in a sensory manner pathologically associated with itself and not in an attitude of excentric position.

Trauma throws light on the nature of pain as an act of being afflicted, by showing that where communication with one's own body has been suspended there is no pain. *If a man is 'beside himself' for any reason, he cannot feel pain.* For when his body has been *estranged*, the raging and burning within him no longer have any relation to himself.

The second basic form of suffering we called the *state* of being afflicted. The act of being afflicted is a passing event, an incident. Here we are concerned with a state in which pain assumes a far greater empathic, gnostic, and practical significance.

The state of affliction is not simply a continuation of stimulation of the pain receptors. It may be compared to the permanence of a feeling such as joy or displeasure, anger, or fear. The comparison helps us to see how the empathic character of pain is forced to undergo transformation, just as anger or annoyance become different if they last a long time. The degree to which feeling penetrates our personality changes as well as the manner in which we react to it. It is therefore not possible to compare pain lasting a short time with pain lasting a long period, except in the case of slight pain caused by pressure, a sting, or heat. Such pains can be objectified completely and reduced to static sensations, as actually happens in experiments on pain. A certain adaptation is wont to occur in cases like these, and also an irregular increase or decrease of pain, which can be explained in part by peripheral stimulatory processes. We must distinguish between similar decrease of pain of longer duration and getting used to painful impressions such as Basler[102] indicated with regard to going barefoot or handling very hot objects. We are acquainted with similar cases in everyday life: they are concerned with specific parts of the skin only and with certain kinds of stimulation. Here too we get the impression that sensitivity to pain decreases according to the reaction to pain and the attitude to the feeling of pain changes. A person learns to bear it.

This is also valid for genuine 'empathic' pain, which is a symptom of illness or injury and the general cause of the suffering experienced in pain. Nor is a man exclusively concerned with the isolated feeling of pain but with his general state with the fact that he must *endure* it: he becomes preoccupied with the disorganization of his inner functions and his inability to work and to think. If the pain is not too great, he is able for a while to disregard it and pursue other thoughts. In such a way the intensity is diminished. Kant pointed this out in his monograph (edit. by Hufeland): *Von der Macht des Gemüths durch den blossen Vorsatz seiner krankhaften Gefühle Meister zu sein.*[103] The great philosopher relates how he was prevented from going to sleep by pain due to gout in his left foot and how he practised the Stoic method of directing his thoughts on some object and 'so distracted attention from the sensation whereupon the latter very soon became insensible'. Such good advice: 'Don't think of the pain, think of something else' does not always help, however; it does not work with everybody alike. But experience does show that in the case of suffering pain loses its 'empathic' character according as the patient finds some way of freeing himself from the state of 'being afflicted' and so turns the pain into a pure, objective sensation. This has something to do with relaxation, which we spoke of in connexion with pain and movement.

The empathic quality of continual pain lies in the two experiences of being *forced* to endure drilling, cutting, throbbing, pulling, pinching, burning, and so on, without being able to offer resistance, and secondly, in the very senselessness of the disturbance not only to our shattered 'vital' integrity, but also to our mental life.

This empathic quality finds expression, according to the intensity and the particular mood and character of the person concerned, in restlessness, impatience, protest, anger, or perplexity. *Suffering* itself is more passive, as we have already said; it is a state of abandonment; kinetic expressions become less constricted and are replaced by general weariness, as though one were being dragged away without protest.

The feeling of pain is far more constricted than any feeling of pleasure, even physical pleasure, and more so than any forms of mental suffering. The last is so bound up with images, thoughts, recollections, and expectations that its purposeful structure is apparent even in the very impact of experience.

The impelling nature of pain robs its victim of all perspective. The sensation of pain is not sufficiently differentiated to allow us to speak of it: neither thought nor expectation nor hope can alter it in the least. It can only be felt and borne. Other forms of suffering are transparent: they *themselves* undergo *formal transformation* which may result in their being got rid of. Physical pain, on the other hand, is irritating as long as it lasts; in our affliction we feel our own helplessness increasingly. Here lies the greatest pathos of chronic pain. We are surrendered to it without any means of defence, and so utterly abandoned that we are no longer able to reach an equal footing with our pain, to respond by some act or purposeful expressive movement. We can only be 'brave' and resist collapse or tears when our pain impels us to 'capitulate' before ourselves.

Weeping is neither an action nor an expressive movement. It is a personal act, an 'act of inner surrender', as Plessner has shown.

'Pain means being thrown back on ourselves without any means of defence, thrown back on our own body in such a manner that we can find no contact with it. The painful area seems disproportionate and seems to obliterate the other regions. We only consist of tooth, forehead, stomach. Burning, drilling, cutting, stinging, throbbing, wrenching, raging or vibrating, pain descends on us, bearing destruction and confusion like some power whirling down into the depths.'[104]

Nothing *breaks* a man in body and soul so much as physical pain. His 'vital' unconscious reactions are affected. In other circumstances these help him to maintain himself as an 'individual'. His psychic powers are no less affected: his organized thinking, feeling, and willing, which enable him to fill his normal place in the world as a person.

He is broken, but not destroyed; despite his affliction he *is* still a person. This shows that the response to pain must be of a very specific nature indeed, although response is really no longer possible. There is some sort of reaction to every situation, no matter how threatening or dangerous or worrying, so long as the situation makes sense. The situation puts a question to man and he can answer it if he understands it. But chronic pain, *la douleur-maladie*, is of its nature absolutely senseless, inevitable. Its senselessness prevents any appeal to thought, will, or feeling. These cannot supply him with the answer. Pain forces him to stake his person in exchange for the answer, that element, in other words, which embraces the whole life of his soul: more than this, he must respond *with* his whole person. This is the essence of pain: to disrupt man's inner 'vital' and psychic structure with incomparable force, but without attacking his personal existence. Pain does not incapacitate his life as a person.

The nature of pain contains its significance. 'Vitally' speaking, it is without sense, nor has it any bearing on psychic functions. Its meaning is existential, therefore ontological and metaphysical, in what it does for his person. Its purpose is fulfilled in the attitude which the man who is afflicted by it adopts to his own bodily existence, to himself and to the ground of his being in the world, to God. Pain is the touchstone of what is actual and deepest in man. This is not character, the typical basic structure of the individual: it is the person, living through his intentional acts and becoming visible to himself in these.

Reactions to pain such as those we have mentioned, restlessness, irritation, protest, rage, complaints, are all psychological reactions, more or less obligatory. They do not 'mean' anything, they are mere agents, distracting attention from pain, discharging the empathic emotions, above all inducing flight from oneself. They are partly life functions and partly what Scheler calls 'self-functions', which must be clearly distinguished from personal acts: 'Acts are performed, functions perform.'[105]

(iii) WHAT IS PAINFUL

'Pain is nature's cry of distress and call for help in danger. This is true both of the physical and of the moral organism.'

R. V. IHERING[106]

What we call painful or distressing is an experience or event which resembles pain without itself being or causing pain. Everything unpleasant is not painful; thus displeasure and suffering are not always painful. Sensory impressions, feelings, thoughts, even situations, can be painful, but only when they possess certain essential characteristics of genuine pain. If these are lacking then we do not refer to them as painful, but rather as unpleasant, embarrassing, depressing, etc.

If we consider sensory impressions, we are struck with the fact that sensations of touch, heat, and cold after taking hold of or feeling objects can be unpleasant or embarrassing but not necessarily painful. If the pressure, heat, or cold is very intense, then of course pain does appear, but the skin senses themselves do not give a painful impression.

The same applies to smell and taste. They can produce a large number of unpleasant, even repellent, impressions, but they are not painful in the sense of causing hurt. There are 'enticing' sharp smells, substances that have a burning or biting taste, with similar sensations in the mucous membrane of the mouth and nose, and stinging and burning on the skin. This is because the pain receptors in the nose and mouth are stimulated, not the organs of smell or taste. We apply specific adjectives to these subjectively experienced sensations of smell and taste: sharp fumes, burning spices. We do not refer to them as painful. Above all, we distinguish them from *genuine* pain in the nose or on the tongue.

The sense of closeness cannot produce painful impressions, but the *higher* senses can, the senses of distance, sight, and hearing. What is the cause of this? Are colours and sounds able to hurt us because sight and hearing are 'higher' forms of communication with distance?

Light or sound intensity does not cause pain. Sunlight can hurt the eyes and force us to close or protect them, but light itself is not a distressing sensation like a violent green or coarse blue dress. The loud pealing of a church bell can cause the eardrum to vibrate almost painfully, but the sound itself, no matter how strong, is qualitatively pleasant, even beautiful, whereas a soft but wrong note on a violin pains us.

Certain nuances of colour and tone, even inharmonious forms

133

and motions, and chaotic sounds, pain or distress us. The explanation lies in the fact that the higher senses are intended to bring us into contact with forms whose purpose *depends on their differentiated structure. They are the organs of ordered relationship with the outer world, and therefore the only ones which permit aesthetic development. Any disturbance of the aesthetic order is distressing.*

Genuine pain afflicts us and severs the psychological unity of our person; our personal existence is unmolested, but it is thrown back on itself and subjected to the destruction of all meaningful associations. In the same way colour, sound, confused lines and movements, and chaotic noises can attack the aesthetic order which we experience in the world through our higher senses and which appeals sympathetically and aesthetically to our emotional disposition. We are then afflicted, hurt, disorganized: above all we are *helplessly* surrendered to what is in itself senseless and destroys sense in other things. Optic and acoustic sensations force themselves on us like pain; they inhibit us in a senseless manner, they irritate us like genuine protopathic impressions. Painful sounds and visual sensations like these are not localized, that is, they have no proper place in an ordered whole, which epicritical impressions always have.

Here we would refer to E. Straus:

'Penetrating noises,' he writes, 'increase in volume if we are in strange surroundings but diminish if we are at home in them. When we enter a room full of people we are overwhelmed with the noise of voices. The noise is all the more distressing the less we feel ourselves part of the assembly.'[107]

If we should come across somebody we know well and like to talk to, the situation immediately changes. The noise of voices seems to ebb away and make 'room' for personal conversation. When it is over the noise starts afresh. A person who shuts himself off from the world becomes sensitive to every sound. Many sick people complain of their hypersensitivity to noise; this is an expression of the disturbance in their communication with the world, not a symptom of functional change in their auditory nerves.

Little need be added to E. Straus' remarks. Painful impressions in the sensitive area of the higher distance senses have the essential characteristics of pain: senselessness, interrupted communication, obtrusiveness and helplessness, abandonment in our affliction: these are derived from the injury to our organization and the fact that we are incapable of responding adequately. The 'pathetic' character of suffering is also a quality of painful sensory impressions and depends on the attitude, that is, the will, of the person concerned. Its painfulness is less stable, less obligatory, especially so when it springs from an aesthetic attitude and not from pathological deviation, depression, or psychasthenia.

Suffering only appears in the personal reaction, that is, in the manner in which a person responds to his experiences. Neither quality, extent, duration, nor intensity of the stimuli can explain physical pain and the distress caused by sensory impressions in the aesthetic sphere. Persons who are over-sensitive to pain do not possess a smaller threshold of response to a stimulus, as we have seen; rather their reaction and their defence are stronger, and they suffer more deeply from their inability to ward off pain.

Greater sensitivity to pain seems to be associated with a 'higher' stage of development and greater refinement, since the reaction of primitive peoples to painful stimuli is less marked than that of civilized peoples. Among the latter there is a striking difference between the less developed and the so-called intellectuals. But, as we have already said, the meaning of a higher stage of development and greater refinement is in itself a problematic question. The field is extensive, but the solution lies in man's relationship with the world, which determines his state of health and general outlook as well as his sensitivity. At any rate we can reject the earlier view that human types, peoples, and classes, etc., differ in their emotions and activities, etc., on a basis of different combinations of quantitatively variable characteristics.

Pain is a destructive state of affliction in one's own organism; it is distressing in that it attacks a formed living unity which to our mind represents a particular sphere and is the scene where our personal life takes place. Hitherto we have spoken of the aesthetic sphere. Let us now see how man can be afflicted in the ethical sphere.

Almost as imperceptible as the harmonious order which determined our physical relations to the outside world is the moral order, the norm of human attitudes and conduct. We are as little aware of it as we are of our bodily structure, as long as our actions are confined to daily repetition, and everything goes its appointed way. Moral laws and principles require no conscious representation in order to serve as the basis of our activity, any more than the laws of spatial localization or principles of muscular innervation when we walk.

Despite the essential differences between the 'vital' and ethical spheres, both in regard to origin and relationship to self, a distinct ethical *life* exists, unified and regulated from within. It pursues its own course without our noticing it, despite our own silent participation. But should this spiritual and natural moral order be upset, we would indeed notice it; the effect on us would be immediate and deep. Should it continue, it would embarrass, torture, and oppress us, we would become sick and irritated and suffer. In every sphere of 'vital', aesthetic, and ethical values a man can be happy and he can be painfully afflicted and suffer. We can withdraw from the 'vital' sphere as long as life takes a 'normal' course but we can do so by means of a special 'technique' (p. 66), by getting beside ourselves with rage or ecstasy and by a pathological relationship to our tasks in the world, by hysteria.

Man's personal participation in the ethical sphere is shown in his behaviour in the community and also in the expressive emotions which accompany it. How far we ourselves are personally present within the ethical sphere of life depends on two factors: first, on our individual sensitivity, which is determined by the differentiation of ethical conditions, and on our *will* to

136

maintain these as a 'norm' in all their subtleties; second, on our acceptance of the ethical organization as the *true* actual normative basis of our personal actions. Unless we acquire ethical principles in such a manner that they determine our behaviour, they are not an inherent part of the character, they do not affect us, nor are they, as it were, the sounding board of our emotions. A person convinced merely by reason that he must honour his parents but who does not really respect them as persons is not affected when his father or mother receives an insult. Conversely, a person affected by such a case discovers thereby how much he really honours his parents, although perhaps he did not realize this before.

In the same sense the criterion of an ethical character is the feeling of being affected when someone else—or more especially in the case of oneself—sins against the moral order, upsets, injures, or violates it. Thus it is a criterion of life that it is able to encounter resistance in the form of an affliction, an affective injury not as a mechanical obstacle to free movement. Any injury to life is painful for the subject who experiences it as a living being.

Pain is not so much a barking watchdog of our health as a cry of distress at the violation of order; a natural law cannot be violated but a norm can, or a law that is respected as a norm. *Thus an analysis of pain shows that what we call the 'vital' should be regarded as a particular manifestation of an ethical order rather than as a specific instance of conformity to the laws governing the 'vital' sphere.* Painfulness is therefore an insult and injury to the sense of what is right although it should affect our own person; it is a 'blow to the heart', the most central and violent possible. It resembles an acute attack or injury done to what is most precious in our personal existence, and we notice in it the three typical effects of physical injury: inevitability of impression, 'dynamization', accentuation of the self-conscious.

The insult offered to the sense of what is right is not only an *act* of affliction, an acute pain like a sting: it is also a *state* of affliction, a chronic pain in the full extent of its pathic, gnostic, and practical significance. There is no pain which can cause greater suffering than that which injures our ethical sense nor one which gives us greater occasion to exercise self-control over our suffering (which we shall examine more closely), or is more prone to mental disorganization and disease.

We are fully justified in using the phrase 'painful insult', for it helps us to perceive that the emotion is not wholly identified with the physical pain, for all its near relationship. It is not a question here of differences in quality or intensity but of the *relationship* between pain and its ground. This point deserves our attention.

If an organ is painful, as a tooth or a muscle, this is not the same as when something pains. Painful means similar to pain, but not identical with it. When we speak of part of the body being painful, we really mean that the undefined sensation is not *actually* pain in the present circumstances, but that it can *become* so at the slightest touch or pressure. Painfulness is thus not only similar to pain but to what is not yet pain and which can turn into it if a missing element is added. What is missing is not quantitative, it is not a difference of intensity in the sensation: it is a sign intimately connected with the circumstance that the painful part must not be touched. The difference between pain and painfulness is expressed in the greater lack of stability in the latter, a greater degree of dependence on circumstances and awareness. It is not yet the essential distinction, which is that we are much more conscious, in the case of a painful sensation, of the *cause of pain*. Thus painful means arousing or causing pain. We can speak of a bandage or a shoe or incision being painful. These conceptual expressions raise two further problems, one narrower in range, namely how far pain teaches us something objectively, that is, possesses the functions of a sense organ, and a more extensive one concerning the objectivity of emotional signs.

With regard to the first, let us call to mind a remark made by

v. Kries on somatization (p. 54): 'A small piece of coal or sand in our eye is felt as a painful object. Considered impartially, this cannot be seen as anything other than a typical example of objectivization of a painful sensation.'[108] Similarly we see the sharpness of the needle and the burning of fire in pain. Actually this is not so much objectivization of painful sensation as sensing properties relating to things *while* in painful contact with them. We owe this distinction of course to the relative *freedom* of our reflecting attitude, whereby we are enabled to experience sensations both as expressions of our community with things as well as marks of their existence and their objective qualities. The following example is intended to clarify the problem of objectivating emotional characteristics. We are acquainted with the bitter taste of quinine and yet it is not a quality of the white powder in the same degree as the unpleasant taste is an intrinsic part of cod liver oil or castor oil. To an animal, presumably, *everything* has emotional attributes, but for us there is only a small group of things with 'pathic' attributes. If we refer to something as being warm or cold, then the qualities of these objects have only a meaning in our association with them. On the other hand, water for the thirsty and food for the hungry possess 'pathic' qualities. In the same way certain events and states are painful. A situation, a meeting, a silence, a word, a refusal to salute, etc., are all painful in their objective and concrete form. Thus we speak of the hurtfulness of a word that causes us pain.

It is important that part of our body can never be for us an 'object' without reference to our own *being*: never a thing with a particular form, colour, or consistency, in space: it is always a movable part of our own body, which we can put in motion when we wish. What we cannot put in motion, like our intestines, does not move us and does not affect us. In pain our relationship with this part is empathic, since pain is the act of being afflicted, affecting our psychophysical constitution, constituting an 'effort', an activity, even if it is powerless—*un effort impuissant*.

Injury to the ethical order, in which we exist as persons and which exists in our own person, is disorganization, it is the experience of a '*malum*', an evil—as something futile—to which we react with resistance and defence. The more powerless the latter is, the stronger are the expressive movements which represent it. The association of phenomena is intimately related to that occasioned by physical pain. Reaction to a painful injury of our sense of what is right arouses the same restlessness, protest, anger, weeping, even the same cry, as violent physical pain.

But how can an insult cause real sensations of pain? Why does a person feel under his hair or in his breast such pain as pressure or constriction? It is a well-known fact that nearly all emotional states are accompanied by alternations in the functioning of the heart and breath, just as, conversely, such changes affect the emotions. *Pain however only appears in the case of very strong unfulfilled desires.* The classic example here is the pain of love, suffering from a broken heart. Heart pains and feeling of constriction can accompany fear as well. The concept of 'somatization' of feelings or physical projection throws as little light on this matter as Scheler's general statement: 'Mental feelings affect our whole being.'

A study of the extensive literature on the interaction of physical and psychic phenomena only furnishes us with a number of not particularly lucid facts (v. Wyss, H. F. Dunbar),[109] confirming us in our conviction that despite new experimental data and careful observations, the fundamental relationship between our personal and physical being has been overlooked. It is only recently that the influence of psychoanalysis and a renewed study of expressive phenomena have enabled us to return to a field of knowledge closer to antique thought than to positivist science.

We cannot give a satisfactory answer to the above-mentioned problem of heart pain and lack of breath, but we can prepare an answer, since apart from emotions, affects, moods, and all the various states which psychology distinguishes, there is also such a thing as a consciousness of our own existence which is a *medium* of all mental objects of activity and form of movement. This existential consciousness is in the form of a feeling of freedom and potentiality, of force and endurance: it is connected with congruity or lack of congruity in desires, expectations, striving, and realization.

Man experiences himself as an existing being, physically as well. His awareness of his body is a scheme, physical in the sense of extended, with back and front, above and below, right and left, and is further divided into head, chest, stomach, arms, and legs; these correspond to the various functions which the parts fulfil in our existence. The heart, the author of the circulation of the blood which gives life to all the organs, is not merely objective: it is also associated with our whole activity by means of existential experience. The fact that it beats harder depends on our own personal attitude to working and anticipates our activity. In all forms of helplessness, whether fear, unfulfilled desires, ethical hurt, sense of guilt, man is thrown back on himself and experiences the expression of helplessness in the change in the beat of his heart. Such a feeling and his difficulty in breathing form the pain in his chest and announce the physical inevitability of some ethical injury or desire that cannot be fulfilled.

(iv) THE PERSONAL ANSWER

'Pain is the destruction of self in the body of agony.'   V. GEBSATTEL[9]

We are inquiring about the sense of physical pain and we know now that only suffering itself can supply the answer. We must come to terms with it personally. If this assertion is to do more than simply indicate the *field* where purposefulness of pain is to be found, we must use concrete images to show the intimate relationship between our suffering and our personal life.

141

Personal life is always incomplete, imperfect by reason of its inner contradictions; we must experience it in this way to know that we are human. We do not usually experience our own existence in this manner, we experience it as a continual stream of pleasure and displeasure, a series of events in and around us, varying according to colour and mood. Against such a background, pain is wholly senseless and incomprehensible. It swoops down on our existence—and then the fissure closes up again. Life wriggles from its grasp. In such helplessness does pain exhaust itself in an animal, whose cry and writhings and ineffectual efforts to get rid of it symbolize its impotence. If the pain continues, the animal's cry is succeeded by groans of endurance, by a dull silence; this is impersonal suffering, a state of passive abandonment.

Man must live like an animal to a certain extent, like a prisoner in the stream of events in and around him, since he is part of transient nature. Even his thinking—although potentially it can withdraw itself—remains bound to life and can do little more than recapitulate what has already taken place. In this sense Max Picard's phrase can be applied to man living an impersonal existence: according to him, the animal is 'totally un-present, always under way, as it were, from one transformation to the next'.[110] Man thus remains a prisoner in the present moment. What has gone is past, what will pass is future. In between there is this present moment, not timeless, but a sort of movable point accompanying us in the stream.

But man is not an animal, even though his life should appear to have an animal form. Man is a person, even as an unconscious innocent child. His humanity is shown in his response to pain, not in his forced cries and groans, but also in weeping, which is an involuntary but strictly personal reaction. Man as a person capitulates when he cries, he is not momentarily struck by displeasure, but he is actually forced into an extreme existential situation and he has *nothing* left that he can do. Then he capitulates, and weeping is, as we have said, a genuine act, one of 'inner surrender', as Plessner puts it. Only a human being is capable of acts such as these.

An animal does not weep, even in pain, since it is not a person, no matter how developed its intelligence and emotional relations to its environment may be. A human being crying from pain does so *as* a person, even though he does not know it. The act of weeping bears witness to man's personal existence, showing that he can never be completely absorbed by the flow of time, the passing moment. His tears demonstrate that in suffering he *is*— he is not absorbed in nature's course but stands outside it, although helpless and against his will. Man reveals his position, even though it is weak, since he has given in when he weeps, contrary to his nature. This act therefore represents the first personal significance of pain, the simplest, weakest, most childish.

Thus in the life of a child, pain has the special function of bringing about weeping which is the first unmistakable testimony of personal being. Man's capitulation when he weeps goes very close to the *limits* of necessity and therefore of what is natural, so much so that in the case of a child who is not yet able to speak we might tend to interpret its tears as a necessary reaction. Yet this is not so. Of course, for a child to cry is what we expect of it, it is part of its way, and in this sense of its nature, but not of *nature* itself. It is a personal act and as such it gives the child self-awareness. Here too it is true that 'the fact of having suffered never passes'.

We have spoken of weeping as a childish reaction, one springing from weakness. It is possible to draw the very opposite conclusion and say that weeping is of small value. A grown-up who is ashamed of tears of anger, joy, or happiness seems to share this belief. And yet in such a case the surrender of oneself can be an act of the most sublime personal response, such as is not the case in tears of pain. To weep for anger, joy, wonder, or delight, besides being an act of self-surrender, is also a recognition of the concrete power of the situation; it is therefore a genuine and spontaneous testimony of man's worth, at whose loss men weep, a witness of the grace of happiness conferred on us or the great power of beauty to delight. Even the tears of a child at some passing pain point to what is most noble in man. With deep respect we let our minds dwell on Christ's tears at Lazarus' grave.

Pain acquires a second significance in personal life towards the end of childhood, when the child learns to *control* itself and not to cry at pain. At first it is so overwhelmed by the emotional force of the situation that it is completely dependent on it, whether it actually bursts into tears or only threatens to do so. At an early stage however a constitutive factor is added to the situation by its will, and it either gives vent to its tears or resists them. The teacher develops this resistance, at first by encouragement, then by admonishment and by pointing out that resistance is more worthwhile. The environment and finally the young person himself demand that he should be brave and not cry at pain and capitulate, but pull himself together and be a man.

The demand is certainly justified for the child, too, to a certain extent. We realize that the scale of suffering is a large one in human life and that both small and great suffering have their adequate forms of expression, which secure an order of experiences so that full value is derived from them. A person must keep his tears for real anguish and not shed them on any occasion. The demand for self-control is part of one's education in courage, and the small unpleasantness must be accepted willingly for the deeper suffering which is the lot of all of us. Physical pain and its passing manifestations have a meaning for the person whose character—the secure system of principles and values to which we turn in personal decisions—is formed by them. A child learns not to want to weep because weeping is unworthy of it.

As we said, the demand for self-control and resistance to capitulation is justified to a certain degree. It should not become severe or obstinate, as an observant teacher knows can be the case even in childhood. Otherwise pain acquires negative significance in the growth of personality.

A strong person firmly rooted in his own character is in no way bound to a rigid system nor insensitive to the relative nature of reality and his own experiences. Character is undoubtedly moderation, though this in the organism means a balance of parts, only possible as a *Gestalt*. A human person is not a *Gestalt* in isolated independence, but in his dependence, his ability to be hurt, even to be destroyed. Besides the relative value of self-control the child must be conscious of the fact that other forces exist which offer an alternative attitude to that of self-discipline. It is a part of the metaphysical mystery of suffering that a force such as this overwhelms us in physical pain that exceeds a certain degree of intensity and duration. It is both *a priori* certain and empirically true that a child who never cries even in violent pain is pathologically hard or obstinate and that this may endanger its harmonious development.

To bear pain bravely, without a sound or tear, may be esteemed as strength of character, as self-consciousness and self-discipline, and be regarded as the highest natural virtue by every human being; yet it is remarkable that it is a 'manly' virtue, and less highly esteemed among women. This should warn us against regarding the significance of pain to be the cultivation of a *heroic* attitude and nothing else.

If a woman is seen as the manifestation of another aspect of human existence in the world, then manly qualities must predominate in a concrete harmonious man. But womanly care and devotion to one's neighbour, her sensitivity and readiness to capitulate—if not in pain—must also be present as a *potentiality*, which can be expressed if circumstance requires. Thus the heroic attitude already considered with reference to the child is only a relative fulfilment of the significance of pain. Pain is also the occasion of suffering and the attitude to suffering in general can also be expressed in one's attitude to pain. This denies the beneficial effect on children of teaching them to bear unpleasantness and want to keep back their tears when they are in pain.

No 'brave' man or woman weeps at pain. The potentialities of the heroic attitude are too little tried and appreciated in the education of children and people of the bourgeois epoch now appearing to near its end: at all events, the personal significance of suffering, physical too, cannot be fully accomplished in its present form. If self-control is regarded as the *sole* worthy reaction, as the *highest* virtue, then, although the demand not to capitulate to pain be justified in itself, it prevents other means of reaction from developing.

Among most primitive peoples, the youths—and sometimes the girls as well—must prove themselves able to endure pain and even torture without flinching, before being admitted to adult circles. This marks the completion of their education, and the function of pain is accomplished. The only remaining form of reaction to other forms of suffering is usually that of surrender, if not tears, at least despair or depression.

In the attitude of antiquity to suffering, the heroic struggle against pain sent by the gods and the *Moira* reigning above them evolved into a noble cult (cf. Scheler[111]). The hero of antiquity did not flee, he actually sought suffering in adventure, danger, and difficult tasks, as though it were a knightly opponent whose conquest in battle, patience, and perseverance tested his powers and his ability—in his own eyes and those of the world. He sought the fame of one who could overcome suffering. 'But this heroic outlook had narrow limitations. It failed when faced with the deeper suffering of the soul, which does not yield to will-power.' Thus even the ancient heroic attitude ends in hardness and bitterness, in oppression and pride, which are only increased by the hero's dependence on the image that others, and undoubtedly he himself as well, have drawn of his stature and heroism.

Nietzsche shows clearly in his *Beyond Good and Evil*[112] that the nature of such pessimism is bitterness and hate employing the mask of spiritual nobility.

'The spiritual pride and revulsion of every man who has suffered deeply—all but determines *how* deeply men can suffer . . . this pride of the chosen one born of knowledge, the pride of the "initiated", of the one who has nearly been sacrificed, requires all forms of disguise to protect himself from contact with intruders and sympathizers and from everything not his equal in pain. Deep suffering ennobles: it separates.'

Whoever has read the touchingly simple description of wounded soldiers in George Duhamel's *Vie des Martyrs* will not accept what Nietzsche says. Nietzsche's romantic lack of realism is blind to the true quality of suffering man. Suffering does not ennoble or separate, except superficially by pride. To be true, Duhamel did see a wounded man who was unaffected: 'His face frozen and burning with hatred and a narrow regard for his dignity', and he recounts of him: 'He suffered courageously as though using his *amour propre* to crush the legitimate reactions of his injured flesh. I can hardly remember having heard him cry out, although this would seem to me most natural. . . .' Is not the utmost limit of human endurance of pain even for the bravest contained in these simple words?

'In Germany, the pure heroism of Kant, Hegel, and J. G. Fichte *necessarily* led to pessimism. There is a limit to the deeds which heroism demanded with disregard of all else. The limit lies in the idea of a word which is metaphysically no longer worthwhile.' 'The "absolute" hero is no longer a hero; he is a fool or a sick man suffering from algophilia,' declares Scheler, whose words, although referring to suffering in general, remind us that even bravery in pain is relative and is of value only as a transitory stage towards an even more perfect personal state which does not end in pride, resignation, or pessimism.

In the course of human development all experiences, and in particular suffering, acquire gnostic and reflexive significance in addition to their 'pathic' significance. If capitulation is a more or less obligatory reaction, to pull oneself together and refuse to surrender is primarily a personal act whereby a man tries to realize some value, namely his own personal worth. The experience of pain offers an opportunity to the mind and the will to develop heroic self-consciousness by a deed. In a certain sense this causes what is painful in pain to merge in the sense of one's personal worth: its positive and active character soothes the distress caused by suffering and at times even gets rid of it.

The essence of pain we showed to be a state where man is afflicted in his most intimate unity, his psychophysical nature: self is brought into conflict with the body while remaining bound to the body in its painfulness. The possibility of a reflexive attitude, of personal reaction to pain, is given in this very *form* of helplessness, this 'destruction of self in the body of agony'.

This is the active heroic reaction, resistance springing from the immanent nature of pain itself in conflict with the organism's innate impulse to protect itself. From this, the heroic attitude derives: it is the expression of the *will* to resist destruction, as necessarily revealed in *personal* life. As we have seen, pain is experienced in the form of an *attack* on existential freedom and is met with a counter-attack, anger, and symbolic struggles of helpless rage. This type of pain reaction leaves its mark on the act of pulling oneself together which is the basis of active and courageous endurance.

A man 'stifles' pain by offering resistance, by pluck; the physiognomic image of a tensed expression and clenched teeth and fists shows a crabbed state of mind appropriating to ill-temper. The heroic attitude must not only be on guard against the 'pride and disdain' of which Nietzsche speaks, but also against hardness, bitterness, and antagonism, which ends in misanthropy. These are the consequences, according to Scheler, of the cult of heroism.

The importance of any human function lies in its ability to fulfil the aim of the organism: namely to *be*, to resist destructive change from within and without. The same is true of the person, although existence in this case is exposed to threats very, very different from those to which an animal or plant is exposed. In nature, action and reaction affect each other according to *necessary laws*. In the human sphere there is a further factor to be taken into account: the *normative* relationship between the unity of the person and intruding forces. The answer to this is something that is both task and fulfilment at the same time: it is not only a reaction, it is performing a task and the performance will accordingly be judged in terms of merit or lack of merit.

Philosophic anthropology and its conception of man is our only source of knowing the demands made on man's personal life, and of determining the norms which must be obeyed. If it regards man, tacitly or expressly, as a product of nature, although the most sublime, then this discipline too is subordinate to the maxim of self-preservation and the preservation of the 'species'. Every reaction *not* directed towards the latter end will be regarded, according to this outlook, as *pathological*. Self-preservation in these terms means the will to live as long as possible under the very best possible conditions. Subjectively these are indicated by pleasurable sensations, objectively in so far as they fulfil 'vital' functions which characterize man as a species. It is less easy to say what is meant by the preservation of the *species*. Naturalistic interpretations of man differ very greatly. Whether the good of the tribe, the people or humanity as a whole, is understood by this phrase, or whether cultural, ethical, and social values are included or not, opinion is unanimous in condemning physical pain as senseless and devoid of intrinsic merit. The warning character of pain is appreciated, but only as a signal, not as a source of suffering.

The question of the personal significance of pain and the personal answer to it has less to do with the act of being wounded than with the state, with endurance and suffering. Pain is accepted by the heroic attitude as a positive good, an opportunity to test courage and character, flattering one's opinion of oneself and the opinion others have of one. Such heroism may rise above the shackles of vulgar naturalism and utilitarianism and furnish men with a norm. The doctrine of heroism in neo-classicism and romanticism was an estimable attempt to free European civilization from the yoke whose ideals were no more than enjoyment and leisure. But for the delicate ethical structure its results were disastrous. Love and simplicity, the secret bonds with the Absolute Being which is a personal God, strive unceasingly towards perfection and true freedom. In the cold climate of pessimism and pride, they wither away. Religion seeks these bonds in the service of God and the imitation of Christ. Because of its final principles, it is unable to regard manliness and a heroic attitude as the highest fulfilment of man although it does not dispute the relative merits of such qualities.

Pain can be borne with heroic courage: this does not get rid of *real* existential distress. Consciousness of pain fades in the aura surrounding the image of the courageous and suffering hero of romantic fantasy. But romanticism is a lack of reality. The heroic attitude by-passes the hidden nature of man and of pain. It cannot but do harm to the ethical value of personal being. Humility is superior to heroism, it is true nobility of the soul, a 'mode of love, and, like the sun, the only means of melting the ice which pride has girded around the empty self'. 'Humility is the deep art of the soul to relax completely, but to a far greater degree than ever attained by mere swimming on the tide.'[113]

Heroism needs such supreme humility to justify itself and guard against pride and pessimism, for humility is totally free from romantic illusion. Heroism as a doctrine and philosophy of life goes back to a childhood reaction when we overcame helplessness inflicted on us by pain in interfering with our activities and functions: we were 'brave' instead of giving in to the disorganization threatening us. This means that the person continues to be active and increasingly gathers inner strength in proportion to the violence of the pain. So pain arouses resistance, not suffering. As we have seen, this form of reaction is given potentially in the moment of experiencing pain.

Is the same true of endurance, passive heroism? Can the characteristics of pain as found in the natural course of events explain this type of personal answer as well? A fact to which we have already referred may help us here: an animal in pain stays still and submits to its pain. Man is also aware of the association between pain and rest as a means of getting rid of the former.

In considering active relaxation and Yoga technique we saw the soothing effect of such practices on the conflict between the subject and his own sense of having a body. For the body is no longer experienced as one's own body in the normal manner. In proportion as the emotional outlook is replaced by an 'objective' one, pain vanishes. The essence of pain lies in the subject's being separated from the body yet at the same time chained to it: thus we can understand the possibility of this separation, or the suffering ensuing from it, being got rid of 'gnostically'.

An animal of course does not keep still as a result of reflection and rational insight: the fact that it does so is a mark of the shadow of intelligence, indeed of the wisdom to be found in so many purely 'vital' reactions. Man only arrives after long efforts, and then only in part, at results which function by themselves in the natural order. An animal forgets naturally; man only with a great effort. We spoke of rest as the somatic equivalent of composure (p. 57); we might add that *rest* is an inherent part of nature's wisdom, of which individuality is a part. *Composure*, on the other hand, is a part of personal life in isolation and must be continually re-won through the agency of the reason and the will. Natural composure in face of helplessness is non-existent just as natural heroism. It is always the product of mind, of culture—even among the most primitive—and is carried on by historic tradition to every succeeding generation and individual as a meritorious form of behaviour. It must be discovered, tried out, and acquired personally.

The personal meaning of pain is fulfilled in an even deeper manner in passive heroism, because *surrender, not* resistance, is the intentional point of departure in this type of personal response to pain. Resistance, the negative answer, which is a *direct* return to being oneself through the agency of the mind by evaluation and

PAIN AND EXPERIENCE

an act of the will, *rescues existential safety and independence in the modality of antagonism*. Although its primary intention is opposition to '*malum*' (pain in this case), it becomes sullen and hard in the manner of reaction of an animal, at least vis-à-vis the man in suffering. Although such a reaction can be a virtue and even an admirable force in a whole people, it is more part of the 'vital' sphere in man than a true personal response to pain. It is of less effect than composure. The latter is man's *positive* response to what is happening to him, as positive as listening is: both have all the outward appearances of idleness. A factor of the will is present in the act of positive transfer, of surrender. Selfless and open, expectant and trusting, quite contrary to animal naturalness, it also shows itself in selfless love. It is the axle on which thinking turns, it is its path and the source of warmth which feeds it.

Composure is not identical with a form of love. It makes love possible. It is a realization of the deepest nature of man in a way in which we can renew our whole personal existence. Composure indicates primarily the relationship of pain to body and soul. We reflect more deeply and are freed from emotional blindness. We are thus justified in regarding composure as a deeper personal response to, as well as a more mature realization of, pain's significance than active heroism. This response is not exclusively manly, nor yet childish. It matures and bears fruit in what in the fullest sense of the word is the *human* sphere.

The association of this form of reaction with emotional life as a whole enables us to understand why it, rather than heroism, should form the basis of extensive and widely differentiated theories of suffering, and why, in personal existence, the bonds between it and religious and ethical life should be so close. The paradox of composed endurance lies in the fact that whoever accepts pain without resistance does in fact experience existential distress and the whole extent of destruction, *and* still triumphs over it. To accept and endure pain with composure is more than just a theory; it is a technique of the life of the soul, which can only be acquired with great effort, as the millenniums of Buddhist philosophy prove.

In practically all forms of *mental* suffering, rational objectivization and resignation lead to apathy or an illusory denial of the reality of suffering. By interpreting it in terms of punishment, warning, or test, the character of suffering can be diminished and even got rid of altogether. This method is of no avail with physical suffering, which cannot be forgotten and which remains unaltered and inevitable; agony in the body and through the body which has revolted against self and from which self cannot escape. Not thought, but action, personal action, in which man transforms himself, can cause pain to shed its character of suffering, overcome the conflict with the body, and regain freedom.

To the unconscious animal nature has given opportunities which man can only achieve by conscious effort; these are: to resist the evil and to get rid of resistance. A third way to realize the significance of pain lies in man's ability to provide a personal answer.

If we regard pain in animal life as a *disturbing* influence, it follows that the only possible reaction to it is resistance, warding off, flight, or accommodation to it and passive surrender. But pain does not interrupt the course of life from without alone: it springs from life itself when the urge to expand threatens to cross the appointed boundaries.

Such a tendency is pronounced in individual being where life has already assumed a sublime form, that is, in individual autonomous existence where it expresses itself in so forceful a manner that to check it would constitute resistance. Scheler speaks of the ecstatic urge of plants to grow. That is not correct. In the course of their growth plants never overcome resistance nor transgress boundaries. They only appear to do so when seeds ferment or plants burst into bud in spring. The individuality of the plant is not centred and therefore there is no boundary for it to transgress. Plants are at the mercy of their environment and their life is a constant adaptation, without the possibility of resistance or opposition. In this sense the plant is the lowest and most harmonious form of existence.

Animals are limited. The fact becomes more apparent the more highly developed they are. An animal possesses inner criteria and is a compact form. Both of these characteristics cause it to come into opposition with other things, such as the outside world and everything that is strange and potentially antagonistic. The animal's urge to assert itself, even the simplest impulses such as hunger and thirst, meets with resistance. If a limit were not set to animal existence and its relative lack of harmony vis-à-vis the outside world, this could not be. Harmonious unity means being bound to a certain basis which itself is the guarantee of unity. So the animal's form of existence shows how the different kinds of suffering are not just disturbances from without: they are immanent in life itself.

Every impulse and every desire is directed towards something which is not, something lying outside one's possession on the other side of a barrier or boundary. This must be transgressed: to do so may cause hurt. Warden[114] actually worked out a method proving that the strength of an impulse can be measured by the duration and intensity of the pain which is not quite sufficient to put the animal off pursuing what he desires. Everywhere in nature, including the sphere of sex, we find pain being accepted, especially among the higher animals, *in order* to achieve what is desired.

Here is a relationship between 'vitality' and pain differing in all essentials from the other cases of pain arising from external stimuli. In a certain sense pain is accepted in overcoming resistance to a drive *for the sake of* something else, namely the desired thing. Although it would be inadmissible to suppose such human behaviour to exist among animals, we can envisage a situation in which the animal appears to choose between two alternatives: the '*malum*' and the '*bonum*', that is, the pain to be expected and the satisfaction to be obtained by accepting it. The situation of the animal is similar to that of a man ready to undergo an operation in order to be cured of some disease. In reality, however, the tension between pain and drive cannot be explained in this way.

An animal is not a subject with a will and reasoning powers brought face to face with his pain or drive. It is not the actor, it is the stage on which the drama is played. Undoubtedly it experiences its own appetites subjectively and the cause of the drive as well as the pain felt in overcoming resistance separating it from its desire. But it must take the form it does and is in no way the result of a free transcendental choice. Accepting pain in order to satisfy an impulse is just as natural as flight from a painful stimulus or keeping still when injured.

The connexion between pain and impulse is reflected in the subjective experience: it does not determine it. We must now try to discover and explain the connexion of the human drives and say why an *objective* relationship can exist, apart from subjective feelings of desire or pain, between the transgressing of boundaries and the individual organization of these drives. We refer to the relationship between procreation and death. Where new life rises from old in procreation, in copulation and birth, we see individual existence resisting its independence and sacrificing itself objectively. Its own organization is disrupted, it may even be destroyed. Such self-sacrifice has been so striking that from antiquity onwards nature has been regarded from the viewpoint of a subjective offering, of acceptance of death in order that the species may be preserved.

Since Darwin we speak of a *striving* to preserve the species, stronger than the impulse towards self-preservation. We must not apply this idea to animal life where there is no such thing as freedom and an excentric mental outlook. The relationship between self-surrender and preservation of the species is not psychological but ontological. We must realize this in order to be able to view the problematic connexion of procreation and pain, to understand why human beings and higher animals suffer pain at birth. These pains cause the sufferer to feel a sense of 'self-destruction', but mingled with the sensation is a conscious and secret sense of pleasure.

In the case of human beings we find that birth-pangs, however violent, are still connected with the objective event: they are experienced in reference to this. They are the literal expression of the narrow gateway leading to release into the broad expanse of life. The pains are accepted as such just as though the life stream were first blocked before entering its broad free bed.

What is the purpose of pain at birth? It lies exclusively *in the opportunity given to the suffering woman to participate directly and consciously in the objective process of a new life coming into being and freeing itself from the old one: the mother may actually sacrifice herself for the new life.*

Pain in personal life is thus not limited to developing a worth-while personal outlook, as courage or composure. Pain realizes its true purpose if the individual involved participates con-sciously *through* its agency in the *reality* of some dramatic event. Then tension is dissolved and life conquers new spheres. A woman is not merely made to reflect on her part in the great drama of life by the violent pains she endures. The quality of what she experiences expresses the 'existential' bond of genera-tions joined by ties of blood. This bond must be severed to enable each generation to have a life of its own. Innumerable women have attested to the positive value of the birth-pangs they have suffered, completely conscious, for the sake of their child.

Organic expansion always causes a rift in the limits imposed on a given structure. In the conscious person the result can be pain. There are two reasons why this should be. Firstly what are known as growing pains, the result of incongruence between the expansive urge and the elasticity of the boundaries; and secondly rupture of the unity: the compact form is lost. 'The same hidden urge of living matter to go beyond itself, to seek *more* and *more* life, expresses itself in the forming of corporations or unions and in procreation. This is the ontological nature of pain' (Scheler).[115]

The experience of pain—which must be conscious, otherwise it would not be pain at all—is *the assertion of the individual's existence in its ontological content. It is forced to take part in the objective life process into which it has been accepted.* A practical example of this, if on a low level, illustrates what is meant: participation in some exciting event. The tension of the audience increases as the play progresses. This is brought about by the events represented developing the tension. The drama leading up to the dénouement resembles formally the rupture of the present order and the birth of a new form of life in a sphere full of potentialities. We notice how the spectator at the height of the tension, when boundaries are about to be transgressed, inflicts pain on himself, pressing his fingernails into his palms and biting his lips.

Surely the reason for this is that such a form of pain is adequate to what is taking place? The spectator is experiencing the same blockage of the life stream before its emergence which we have referred to above. Do we not *seek* pain—in experiencing a drama—in order to participate personally in objective events, to help unravel the tangles which perplex us, so that we too can sense the relief when tension is relaxed?

Our pinching ourselves at the height of dramatic tension could, of course, be explained more simply in terms of *fear*. Pain would then have the function of a distracting stimulus. In many fear situations we meet the same infliction of pain on oneself. Yet it is not dramatic tension which arouses fear but conversely fear which causes dramatic tension. Fear comes at the approach of danger, when a catastrophe is expected. An explosive force is inherent in the situation and at the critical moment it will destroy the old order and create the new. Although a man may be affected by it in a most unpleasant fashion, he is at least freed from fear and paralysing uncertainty. Once more life flows freely towards a new sphere of activity.

Let us look once more at the relationship of pain and impulse and assess their association in the subjective feelings. An unsatisfied urge is always experienced as expectation of release from the bondage of desire. If it is very intense, like great thirst, the contrast between desire and fulfilment resembles the blocking of the life stream and its subsequent outflow and rest. As a rule the passage from such constriction to release is not very clearly perceptible; the moment and the situation always depend on circumstances to which the person can only contribute *indirectly*.

There is one exception: namely sexual desire. Here the orgasm is completely dependent on the subjective attitude and behaviour. The active participation of the individual in what is taking place hastens the release from the drive in the orgasm. Both in the animal and in the human world pain, as we know, is sought and accepted. Numerous psychiatric studies, including the excellent work of v. Gebsattel, show how complicated is the relationship between pain and the sexual impulse, and also how it can become pathological. At all events, the objective bond between surrender and the awakening of new life is reflected in the subjective experience. Here pain represents the straits holding life back till it finds release in the act of surrender.

It is easy to see that a whole series of 'vital' situations exists in which the expansive urge of individual life threatens to cross natural boundaries. In such situations pain enables the individual to participate in what is taking place within himself, so that he can regain possession of himself, though in a different form. Thus pain is the mark of release, aiming at acquiring something of value whose enjoyment is greater than the hurt caused by pain.

We come to the conclusion that pain has both an ontological and a psychological meaning. The former is manifested in experience but *only in so far as the content of the experience is a genuine objective event*. Man is the only creature endowed with the power to experience in the midst of destruction of himself by pain the true ground of pain, death, and sin in humanity. He is able to do this because he has reason and his reason releases his emotional life from the dark forces of desire and brings him to the clarity of the *'raison de cœur'* (Pascal).

Pain shows its true significance in man. This is more than a

warning, signal, punishment, or admonishment, more than a
test or opportunity of developing qualities of courage or patience.
The pain man can experience only acquires a sense of real personal
surrender in so far as he genuinely participates in a fuller existence.
Life is freed from the obstacles standing in the way of its entry
into a new order of freedom: it becomes mature. The solidarity
of a living community endows personal suffering with a peculiar
obligation to lead a community of which one forms part, to lead
it through the narrow gateway to a new life. Such release
demands sacrifice of one's own well-being, acceptance of suffering as the price of peace, and the opportunity to develop in a
wider sphere of existence. Life breaks down its banks in the
medium of the person before flowing into its new bed.

The simplest examples of formal connexion between pain and
human life is the participation of man in the community to
which he belongs by birth and tradition, namely his native
country, and his reaction when the clouds of war make him
expect a transformation of his sphere of life. The suffering of the
individual—and every other form of suffering—is unmistakably
and significantly rooted in the nature of solidarity, not in the
consciousness of solidarity. What is important is not how suffering is borne, whether courageously or in a cowardly manner,
with composure or irritation, but the fact *that* it is endured. The
fact *that* someone fights, is wounded, and dies for his country,
endows his suffering with a significance quite apart from his
own character, temperament, or disposition, just as the merit of
doing one's duty is not determined by talent.

Some people are able to bear pain with courage and composure. Duhamel draws such a man in his wounded soldier
Auger: 'The humble basketmaker from the Charente who did
not seem unhappy in his suffering.' 'He suffered in an intelligent,
enlightened manner, almost methodically.' How is Grégoire so
different? He cannot bear pain. 'Grégoire does not know how to
suffer, just as one does not know a foreign language.' 'Only it is
easier to learn Chinese than to learn the trade of suffering.

Grégoire starts to tremble straightway; the beasts of pain hurl themselves on the defenceless man and tear him to pieces.' 'Auger, why are you touched by grace and why is Grégoire not?' There is a great difference between the two, the brave Auger and the mean, fearful Grégoire. 'It shows a rather naïve desire for equality to assert that all men are equal before suffering. No, no, men are not equal before suffering.' But in one regard both are the same. Both suffered for their country. To be sure, Auger was brave and received the *médaille militaire*. But when Duhamel asked Grégoire how he was wounded, the laconic reply was: 'Down in the plain like the rest.'

'With the rest'—that is the crucial point. It is not the manner of a man's bearing his pain but the *fact* of his belonging that gives pain its meaning. It is the seal of common destiny, the communal character of being wounded and the pain of the one for the many for the sake of something higher. But the mental attitude of the wounded whose suffering seals his bond with the community does allow the purpose of pain to be realized. For the attitude decides whether the basis of the bond is sheer necessity, as in the animal world, or rather the free acceptance of, or at least consent to, the inevitable.

A mother animal sacrifices herself for the sake of her young, the leader of a herd hurls himself into battle for the good of the rest. But this is not a free action; it is done without the animal's realization. It lacks the special admixture which we call *selfless love*, as opposed to greed or instinctive urge. A conflict can take place within the animal's nature, but the animal is not aware of the fact; it screams without protest or suffers in silence without any act of self-surrender. A man who suffers must reflect and be placed face to face with what he is suffering. He can never bear. pain, the yoke of a common destiny, helplessly, as an animal does A man fighting for his country, like Grégoire, 'who does not know how to suffer', will be forced to suffer to a certain extent, but for him it is a vocation to which he responds, because he understands it.

Of course there are the blood witnesses in human life, lambs led innocent to the slaughter, children like the 'Holy Innocents' whom Herod murdered and whose cries of pain, unknown to themselves, helped to save the world. Yet the more fully developed a man's personality is, the greater his awareness that he is participating in something that is objectively meaningful. He is better able to suffer because he has once responded to the order to take his place 'with the rest'. In merely following his nature, he would give in, like a child, or give way to rebellious anger. The *spontaneous human reaction* is very different and depends on character and temperament. Even specifically material factors like tiredness or illness play a constitutive part. The *personal response*, on the other hand, is exclusively determined by participation in the existential distress where man acts 'with the rest'. This personal response *is revealed in pain*.

The purpose of pain lies in its bringing man to himself in the midst of his affliction so that he shares in the distress of the whole community, in their fate and their longing for release. As an isolated phenomenon, as pure feeling, pain is without any meaning. However bravely or composedly we bear it, it is a state of *defenceless* rejection, where we experience the most acute contradiction between personal and physical being.

Pain is distressing because the mind cannot fathom it nor the will overcome it, while desire, even the most powerful, is ineffectual against it. A man in pain is torn and stricken in the innermost structure of his concrete existence. Only a person who has himself experienced pain knows how terrible it really is. Leriche, who watched such suffering for over thirty years, says:

'Always purposeless, it impoverishes man. The most enlightened mind becomes a poor wretch because of it, thrown back on himself, preoccupied with his affliction, selfishly indifferent to everything and everybody, obsessed by the fear that the pains will return.'

'Oh, I know that people can forget their ills and that certain heroic souls manage to dominate their suffering and not show it. I do not disregard what exalted religious and philosophic ideals are capable of.'

'But such an attitude is exceptional, and is only achieved in moments of heroism. Not everyone has a soul of fire; in the reality of human life, even for the great mystics, *the struggle against pain is usurious.*'

With the wisdom of a man in the midst of life, sympathetic and endowed with a sound sense of reality, this surgeon says of pain: 'I feel we must be on our guard against confusing two separate spheres: that of illness and that of religious perception.'
We must indeed keep these spheres apart: pain as illness to which man's nature as well as his soul responds, and pain as a state of existential distress to which he responds as a person. We must allow each of them his own individuality. Man can choose between two attitudes to pain. He can *deny* the reality of the distress and regard pain as a disturbance which he must bear with courage and composure. Or he may *recognize* the distress and accept it as the sign and seal of a deep bond with being itself, with the purpose of this life. Existential distress, wrote v. Gebsattel,[9] can only be grasped in perspective relating it to a more perfect and happy state. We add to this statement and say that a sufferer can only discover the sense underlying the senselessness of pain in so far as he shares in the solidarity of man in nature and sin. St Thomas says: '*Quod caro in peccato concepta subjacet dolori, non solum ex necessitate naturalium principiorum sed etiam ex necessitate reatus peccati*'* (*Summa*, III Q XV, art V. ad 2). Every technique of the soul, whether resignation, hedonistic flight, blunting oneself to a state of apathy or illusionist denial of the reality of pain, has little to contribute to our knowledge of pain and its

* The flesh, conceived in sin, is forced to suffer pain, not only by principles of nature but by reason of necessity imposed by the guilt of sin.

162

purpose in the face of the view which sees it as a just and reasonable punishment for original sin. Natural attitudes and considerations can at most *prepare the path* which the person *himself* must travel. They help to strengthen his courage and his composure, both of which are virtues of character, but they are only aids, not essential to his task of realizing the existential purpose of pain in himself.

We must tread the path of suffering without reservations, knowing that it cannot be shortened nor avoided, even by techniques of the soul which only sooth its acuteness, or its bitterness. Such is the way of 'blessed suffering and at the same time release from suffering through the merciful love of God: the "royal road of the Cross".'

We humbly tread this path and a new world of light and peace opens up before our eyes: a world of which even the masters of Yoga do not dream, a mighty expanse of wisdom higher than reason itself. Happiness increases the further a man travels beneath the goad of pain in the merciful love of God; this path is open to all who are humble of heart. The purpose of pain, the most widespread and genuine form of suffering, is fulfilled in the form of love, the greatest reality in a man's life. 'The cross, the image of love, gives man true pain. For it is the doorway and the dawn of true joy.'[116]

Whoever waits expectantly on the bank of the river of life will be called one stormy night to take on the heavy burden of physical pain, not only with courage and composure, but for love's sake. And he will receive the grace of inexpressible joy when he discovers that in him there has taken place the miracle of Christopher, the simple man.

V

Annex

THE aim of my study of pain has been to consider the theoretical conceptions motivated by scientific research and by the experience of everyday life in health and disease. We have had to accept the fact that the phenomenon of pain cannot be defined in an objective way. This was also the opinion of Sir Thomas Lewis who devoted a great deal of his scientific work to the study of pain. He wrote: 'I am so far from being able . . . to define pain . . . that the attempt could serve no useful purpose.'[117] It is obvious that the essential quality of pain, like all original personal experiences (sensations, feelings, memories, expectations, etc.), can only be known immediately in the course of human existence. This means that pain appears always in a certain *context* that determines the significance of the subjective experience. Particularly is this true of pain. I consider this simple fact the most important result of every research and experiment. Of course there may be a considerable difference in opinion about the *extension* of the context necessary to grasp the full and essential meaning of pain. The reader will have encountered my conviction that the *real* meaning of pain is only manifest in the full context of the existence of man, understood as the general mode of his 'intentional project' of the world. The characteristics of this project depend on his personal history, his relation to 'first principles' (Newman), his system of values, and the meaning given to his bodily sensations.

I should like to add to this English edition of my book, first published in Dutch in 1943, a review of a number of recent publications that may reveal in which direction the modern conception of pain has developed in the various sciences. Of course I shall have to select. The excellent paper by H. K. Beecher[118] on 'The Measurement of Pain' (1957) covers 687 pages. This obliges me to limit my review and I think it may be useful to consider new studies to solve some problems, already mentioned in the foregoing chapters.

(i) A great deal of effort has been made to determine the *threshold* of pain sensation experimentally. Using the Hardy-Wolff-Goodell technique of stimulating the skin by thermal radiation, McKenna[119] found the variability of the threshold of the same order as Hardy found with small groups of highly 'trained' subjects. The influence of training on the results of experiments of pain is described by Hardy and Cattel (1950). Untrained subjects (160 medical students), even of high intelligence, cannot be used successfully to measure the threshold-raising effect of aspirin, etc. (Beecher, p. 136). McKenna has questioned the subjects' judgment of painfulness of the threshold sensation. According to him '78 per cent reported that, based upon their own experience and definition of pain, they would not consider the threshold sensation painful if they encountered it in ordinary life outside the experimental situation' (p. 454). His conclusion is that 'consequently, results obtained in threshold investigation can have no applicability to the human pain problem in real life'. It seems that the difficulty met with in every experimental study derives from the fact that the subject's awareness of pain and the meaning he attaches to it depend on his attitude, attention, and reflection, and consequently on his relation to himself, his body, and to the surrounding events. So we understand the significance of Bishop's remark: 'Pain is what the subject *says* hurts, you can't get behind that' (quoted by Beecher, 1957). In psycho-physiological research many authors have tried to meet this difficulty by distinguishing pain perception and pain reaction.

(ii) *The dual aspects of pain.* It is well known that noxious stimuli involving pain give rise to many reactions, e.g. emotional response, smooth muscle, gland and skeletal muscle effects, disturbances of gastric and colonic and renal functions, cardiac arythmias, elevation of arterial pressure, circulation.[120] We are not surprised that the reaction to pain, unlike the threshold for perception of pain, 'varies between wide limits for given individuals and for the same individual under different circumstances'.[121] Some years ago[122] I pointed out at a medical conference that the notion of reaction to pain contains 'the germ of the entire problem of pain'. The solution of this problem requires a totally different conception of man from that yielded by a neurophysiology based on Cartesian principles or clinically derived theory. 'The physician trained exclusively in natural science will find difficulty in conceiving of the body as a situation.' 'The human body remains the be-souled bodiliness of a person.' 'Even the so-called unconscious reactions are determined by interpretations of impressions of the external world.' I mention these ideas because they help us to understand the results of recent experimental and clinical research. If, for example, we consider the 'dual aspect' of pain, is it remarkable that the reaction pattern often seems to be independent of the awareness of pain?[123]

In an investigation at once clinical and experimental, A. von Auersperg[124] proved that viscerogenic interoceptive pain brings about a morbid transformation in vegetative control. The same author analyses the specific reaction of the abdominal serum on injury, that which Capps[125] long ago described as a 'dagger stab'. It turned out that this characteristic sensation was independent of the manner in which the pain was produced. The perception of pain is related to the function of the injured organs and tissues in such a way that it is artificial to separate them. It seems to me that Wolff and Hardy agree with this view since they write that the reaction component includes the 'quale' or feeling-state 'and represents the individual's response to a given situation based on his own past experience and inborn peculiarities'.[126]

(iii) *There is no sense organ for pain*. 'Even the most thoroughgoing anatomical investigation of pain, including end-organs, afferent paths and tracts in the central nervous system, has not achieved very much. The anatomist cannot point to the nucleus or level in the brain which must be reached by the so-called pain-conducting fibres before there can be consciousness of pain.' These remarks from Cohen[127] are in agreement with the result of modern investigation. Even the very thorough and extensive work of the neurosurgeons James C. White and William H. Sweet,[128] who made a precise study of the mechanisms of pain and of its neural transmission by nerves, states in its Introduction: 'In theory, our present knowledge of anatomy should make it possible for the surgeon to relieve all varieties of intractable pain by specific interruption of afferent pathways, but this is unfortunately far from the case.'

Leriche[129] also concludes recently: 'there are no pain receptors', and Hebb[130] agrees: 'The pain receptors (e.g. in a sound tooth or in the cornea) are pressure-receptors as well.' In his full and accurate investigation the Dutch neurosurgeon Noordenbos concludes: 'There is ample evidence that afferent conduction is *not* along specific fibres . . . and specific receptors . . . are found to be largely absent, except in certain circumscribed areas.'[131]

When we must accept that there are no specific end-organs, specific fibres, or central receptor for pain, we may ask how we can explain the apparent dependence of pain-feeling on the structure and function of the nervous system. Clinical experience teaches that pain may be violent (as in *herpes zoster*) when there is damage to the afferent pathways so extensive as to result seemingly in total anaesthesia.

(iv) *The organization theory* suggested by Hebb attempts to resolve these difficulties raised by the classic conception of a receptor-conductor-effector system. Cohen[132] summarizes Hebb's explanation in a clear way: 'The impulses conducted by "C"-fibres become painful only if they disrupt a well-organized pattern of nervous activity. If these impulses are assimilated into an organized neural action, no pain is felt.' Hebb[133] accordingly states:

'Slow impulses may produce pain (a) because of some peculiarity in the pattern of thalamic activity they arouse (apart from intensity at this level), (b) because the slow impulses are effective in arousing excessive bursts of firing from the thalamus. A theory of pain must provide for the fact that an increase of pain often results from hypofunction in afferent structures.'

Noordenbos,[134] discussing clinical experiences of causalgia, suggests 'the presence of a disproportionate number of uninjured slow fibres in the nerve'. He assumes that a proportion of these fibres travels a short distance via the sympathetic chain before entering the spinal cord. This would explain the beneficial effect of sympathectomy in many cases and its failure to relieve the pain in some instances. I would agree with him that the conception of an imbalance between various fibre groups fails to account for the most important symptom of all, the one which really constitutes the central feature of the disease (causalgia): the *spontaneous pain*'. In his concluding remarks Noordenbos puts his finger, I think, on the real centre of the problem of pain when he writes: 'At present one speaks of the patient's reaction to pain, but would it not be more correct to say that pain is the result of the patient's reaction to this abnormal afferent pattern?'[135]

In my opinion this explanation refers to the fact that the subject as such encounters his inner (bodily) world as well as the outer world in such a way that he is able—between certain (and often narrow) limits—to organize a pattern of impressions and to give them a particular meaning. Not only does common experience suggest that there is activity on the part of the subject in perception, but this activity can also be proved experimentally. In relation to the problem of pain I mention an investigation by Auersperg et al.[136] on the disturbances of sensation caused by ischaemia of a limb. The authors showed that

'in contrast to what might be expected from the intense change undergone by receptors in the muscles during ischaemia, as observed by Matthews, weight discrimination and the capability of hitting targets with objects of different weights were not significantly altered even during the painful phase of fatigue'.

This phenomenon may be compared with the common experience that in tumultuous surroundings (a factory, a crowd shouting and clamouring) we can 'organize' a pattern of sounds so as to be able to understand human speech or follow a melody.

(v) *Psychogenic pain.* In accordance with the organization theory is the statement of Cohen 'that, in the last resort, what matters in causing pain or its absence is the *meaning* of the experience to the organism'. There are many examples—and I have mentioned some in this book—of the influence of the 'psychic state' on pain. Under suggestion a mild touch of the skin may become painful. The influence of anticipation and anxiety on pain has often been pointed out. Analgesic agents reduce this anxiety. Kornetsky[137] found that morphine is extremely effective in raising the threshold of pain when anxiety is present.

Painful sensation can attain a different meaning, even a symbolic one (Mitscherlich and Ruffler).[138] This conception—an extension of the psychoanalytic theory of Freud—is shared by Szasz.[139] He suggests that we should recognize three 'components' or concepts of pain. First, pain can *mean* a signal of danger to the body; this is *intra-personal*. Secondly, pain may be understood as including a request for help from another person; this is *inter-personal* as well. Thirdly, pain may not refer to the body at all but simply signify a request for help, a complaint about unfair treatment, or a demand for punishing a hated object; that is, the 'pain' may exclusively mean an *inter-personal* communication.

It is interesting to note that French authors also emphasize the influence of human relationships on pain. Michaux[140] proposes a 'culture of emotionality' and a 'culture of insensibility'. He mentions 'pain as alibi, pain of hidden chagrin' and gives as examples headache and stomach-pain in emotional situations.

'Pain represents the coded language of moral pain and affective emptiness.'

The effects of social factors and affective experience on pain have been established by many authors, e.g. Curtius,[141] Bürger-Prinz.[142]

(vi) *Some clinical observations.* Clinical experiences have long demonstrated that pain depends more on the emotional state than on the intensity of a stimulus and is therefore more like a 'passion of the soul' (Aristotle) than a kind of perception or a sensation. Beecher[143] mentions that 'great wounds with great significance and presumably great reaction are made painless by small doses of morphine, whereas fleeting experimental pains with no serious significance are not blocked by morphine'. There are many observations to the effect that idiots and psychotics may inflict on themselves horrible mutilations, while they have a normal threshold for pain. Most interesting are the investigations of patients suffering from so-called pain-asymbolia and patients who have undergone pre-frontal lobotomy. Furthermore there are rare instances of young people who are utterly insensitive to pain. Such children display no reaction to injury. The pain asymbolia that is met with in cortico-thalamic lesions, section of the post central gyrus and of the angular gyrus is mostly associated with a disturbed body image. Pain, like painlessness, depends on the subject's relationship to his own body. This pain-asymbolia has been first described by Schilder (1928), and it is a state in which the subject has lost the notion of the meaning of pain, just as in visual agnosia the meaning of optical perceptions is lost. Hécaen[144] states that the patients lack affective resonance to a pain-stimulus.[145]

After pre-frontal lobotomy a similar state is found. Wolff and Hardy[146] mention an observation of Walker concerning a woman with intractable pain associated with an amputation stump. In the months following a bilateral frontal lobotomy she was confused but looked content and complained little. When she was questioned about the pain she stated that the pain was present but that she gave it less attention and it did not concern her. Other patients say 'that the pain is still with them but that they are not bothered by it, or even that the pain is in the room somewhere but they are not sure whose it is' (Cohen). This alienation of bodily feelings is one aspect of the total—and complicated—change in personality caused by lobotomy.

(vii) *Conclusion.* Recent studies of pain seem to me to confirm the fundamental theoretical conception of this book, now made available to the English reader, who will not fail to notice that neither the results of research nor of common experience are compatible with a purely physiological explanation of pain. My view can be put simply: I consider pain a phenomenon intimately connected with the reality of human nature. A deeper insight into this reality teaches us that it is characterized by an ambiguous relationship between the subject and its body. This is 'rationally' incomprehensible. We *are* in a certain way *our* body and we have a body. As Gabriel Marcel has said, we cannot identify our self-being completely with our body and we cannot completely distinguish our 'self' from our body. I believe this French philosopher has spoken truly that: 'The site of pain appears to be the zone where having emerges into being.'

VI

Notes and References

I. PAIN AND ITS PROBLEMS

1. Bossuet, *Oraison funèbre de la Princesse de Gonzague*.

2. Leriche's exposition of the viewpoint of pain prevention is excellent: *La chirurgie de la douleur*, 2nd edit. Masson, Paris, 1940. 'We must give up the notion that pain is beneficial. Pain is always a sinister gift. It lowers man and makes him more ill than he would be without it. It is the strict duty of the doctor always to prevent it, if he can.'

3. Mgr. von Keppler, *Lijdensschool*, Louvain 1927, p. 135.

4. I was unable to obtain access to the publication in question (W. Hartnacke and E. Wohlfahrt, *Geist und Torheit auf Primanerbänken*. Report on the Saxon measures to limit University entrance, Dresden, 4th edit. 1934). The results quoted were taken from the monograph by F. Sauerbruch and H. Wenke, *Wesen und Bedeutung des Schmerzes*, p. 114 (Junker und Dünnhaupt Verlag, Berlin 1936).

5. Léon Bloy, *Le Pèlerin de l'Absolu*.

6. Prof. van Stockum tells me:

Pain: *pina*; Middle High German *pine*; Middle High German *pein* from Latin *poena* (*pena*); Old Saxon *pina*; Middle Dutch *pine*; Modern Dutch *pijn*. Original meaning (Christian): punishment, hurt (only later *pain* meaning wretchedness, agony).

German *Schmerz*: original meaning: stinging, biting pain or wound, referring to both physical and mental upset.

German *Weh*: originally a cry of pain. Germanic *wai* (related to Latin *vae*) became a noun by 800 (in compounds usually in the sense of pain·(Schmerz)).

172

7. 'God replies to the evil of sin (this *"malum quod est culpa"*, of which St Thomas of Aquinas speaks, created by man and hurtful to God), by the evil of pain (this *"malum quod est poena"*, hurtful to man).' Charles Grolleau, 'Quelques propositions sur la douleur', *Etudes carmélitaines*, 1936, 20th year, Vol. II, October, Desclée de Brouwer, Paris.

8. Leibniz, *Lettres*, Vol. I, 43rd letter.

9. V. E. von Gebsattel, 'Süchtiges Verhalten im Gebiet sexueller Verirrungen', *Monatsschr. f. Psychiatr. u. Neurol.*, Vol. 82 (1932), p. 127.

10. M. Pradines, *Philosophie de la sensation II*. La sensibilité élémentaire (les sens primaires). 2. Les sens de la défense, p. 116. (Publications de la faculté des lettres de l'Université de Strasbourg, fasc. 66.) Paris 1934.

11. V. von Weizsäcker, *Handb. d. norm. u. path. Physiol.* XI, 1, p. 57.

12. Among others: *Grondproblemen van het dierlijk leven* (Philosoph. Bibliotheek), Antwerp 1938; *Wege zum Verständnis der Tiere*, Max Niehans Verlag, Zürich 1938; Buytendijk and Plessner, 'Die physiologische Erklärung des Verhaltens. Eine Kritik an der Theorie Pawlows' (*Acta Biotheoretica*, Vol. I), 1935, p. 151.

13. C. Richet, *Dictionnaire de Physiologie*, 1902. Art. 'Douleur'.

14. P. Schilder, *Das Körperschema. Ein Beitrag zur Lehre vom Bewusstsein des eigenen Körpers*, Berlin 1923.

15. E. Straus, *Vom Sinn der Sinne*, Berlin 1935.

16. H. Plessner, *Die Stufen des Organischen und der Mensch*, Berlin 1928.

17. V. von Weizsäcker, *Der Gestaltkreis*, Leipzig 1940.

18. P. Vogel, *Pflügers Archiv.* 228 (1931), pp. 510, 632, and 230 (1932), p. 16.

19. P. Christian, 'Wirklichkeit und Erscheinung in der Wahrnehmung von Bewegung', *Zeitschr. f. Sinnesphysiol.*, Vol. 68 (1940), pp. 151–83.

20. L. Klages, *Grundlegung der Wissenschaft vom Ausdruck*, Leipzig 1936.

21. H. Plessner, *Lachen und Weinen. Eine Untersuchung nach den Grenzen menschlichen Verhaltens*, 1941; 2nd edit. Francke Verlag, Berne 1949.

22. Also quoted in E. Lieck, *Der Arzt und seine Sendung*, Munich 1927. cf. also V. von Weizsäcker, 'Der Arzt und der Kranke', *Die Kreatur*, I (1926), pp. 69–86, and *Medizinische Anthropologie, Philos Anzeiger*, II (1927), pp. 205–63.

23. O. Schwarz, *Medizinische Anthropologie*, Leipzig 1929, p. vii.

24. Leriche shows how senseless the phenomenon of pain is for the doctor too. It is of little help even for diagnosis: 'For doctors living in contact with sick persons, pain is merely a contingent, annoying, burning, hurtful symptom, difficult to suppress, and one which is usually all but valueless for diagnosis or prognosis.' 'Defensive reaction? Happy warning? In actual fact the majority of illnesses, even the serious ones, appear in us without warning. Sickness is nearly always a drama in two acts, of which the first takes place, cunningly enough, in the dim silence of our tissues, with the lights out, before the candles have been lit. When pain makes its appearance we are almost in the second act. It is too late. The dénouement is in train. It is imminent. Pain merely makes more hurtful and wretched a situation which is already irrevocable.

'I ask you, what warning does a neuralgia of the trigeminal nerve give us?

'If nature were concerned about us, if she took care of us in the way she is credited with, she would warn us of the presence of a kidney stone before it is no longer able to emerge in the normal manner, when it is still dust and could be got rid of with ease' (loc. cit., pp. 39–40).

II. THE PHYSIOLOGY OF PAIN

25. J. D. Achelis, 'Der Schmerz', *Zeitschr. f. Sinnesphysiol.* (1925), p. 31.

26. A survey of the physiology of pain is to be found (with references) in the *Handb. der Physiol.* by Bethe, Vol. XI; further, E. von Skramlik, *Beiträge zur Psychophysiologie der Sinnesleistungen. Psychophysiologie*

der Tastsinne I and II, 1937, Leipzig, Akad. Verlagsges; in Dutch the monograph of C. U. Ariëns Kappers, 'De anatomie en physiologie van den pijnzin', in *Psychiatr. en Neurol. bladen*, 1937, pp. 783–809. A good résumé of the experimental data in Piéron, *Traité de physiologie normale et pathologique*, Vol. X, fasc. II, Paris (1935), pp. 1147–85. Reports of new tests in: Harold G. Wolff and James D. Hardy, 'On the Nature of Pain', *Ps. Review* 27 (1947), p. 167.

27. J. Boeke, 'Nerve endings, motor and sensory'. In Penfield, *Cytology and cellular pathology of the nervous system* I (1932), pp. 243–315. J. H. Woollard, 'Intra-epidermal nerve endings', *J. anat.* 71 (1936), pp. 54–60.

28. J. D. Achelis, 'Die Physiologie der Schmerzen', *Der Nervenarzt* 9 (1936), p. 559; idem. 'Der Schmerz', *Zeitschr. f. Sinnesphysiol.* 56 (1925), p. 31.
    P. Hoefer and A. Kohlrausch, 'Über die Schwellenempfindungen an Schmerzpunkten', *Pflügers Archiv.* 205 (1924), p. 447.
    Rowbothan, *Brain* 62 (1939), p. 364.

29. Goldscheider, *Das Schmerzproblem*, Berlin 1920.

30. Y. Zottermann, 'Touch, pain and tickling etc.', *Journ. of physiol.* 95 (1939), pp. 1–28.
    Adrian, *The mechanism of nervous action*, Philadelphia 1932.

31. Lewis and E. E. Pochin, 'The double pain response of the human skin to a single stimulus', *Clinical Investigation*, Vol. 3 (1937), p. 67 (cf. the same journal, pp. 141 and 191).

32. M. von Frey and others are of the opinion that all stimuli free a chemical substance which releases the actual stimulation of the nerve endings sensitive to pain. If this is true it means that there is a difference in principle between them and the sense organs. These react through their organization to a particular stimulus only. This arouses nervous activity. According to Lewis (*Brit. Med. Journ.* No. 4023 (1938), p. 321), the quality of pain does not depend on the stimuli but on the tissues in which stimulation occurs.

33. M. Pradines, loc. cit., p. 116.

34. M. Pradines, loc. cit., p. 116 and p. 98.

35. E. H. Weber, *Tastsinn und Gemeingefühl*, Leipzig 1905.

36. J. von Kries, *Allgemeine Sinnesphysiologie*, Leipzig 1923, p. 15 ff. ' "Somatisierung"; I use this term to designate our referring a feeling to our body, our interpreting it as a physical state. . . .'

37. H. Rothmann, 'Das Jucken und die juckenden Hautkrankheiten', *Jadassohns Handb. Haut- und Geschlechtskrankheiten XIV.–1. 1930.*

38. M. von Frey, *Zeitschr. f. Biol.* 76 (1922), p. 4.

39. K. Wilde, 'Zur Phänomenologie des Wärmeschmerzes', *Psychol. Forschung* 20 (1935), pp. 262, 321.

40. O. Sjöqvist, *Acta psychiatr.* Kbh. 17 (1938), p. 1., cit. in Zottermann, loc. cit., note 30.

41. V. von Weizsäcker, 'Zur Klinik des Schmerzes', *Der Nervenarzt* 9 (1936), p. 555.

42. H. Piéron, *Année psych.* XXVI (1925), p. 151.

43. The so-called neurotic or psychogenic tiredness is not taken into consideration here. Whatever may be its original cause, the feeling is not brought about by real physical phenomena. It is 'imagined'. Imaginary itch and imaginary pain also exist. Usually there is also a very weak stimulation, increased to a stronger sensation by unconscious application. Tiredness, itch, and pain are therefore easily influenced by suggestion. (On physical tiredness cf. also Buytendijk, *Geneeskünd*, Gids 1942.)

44. Jacobson, *Progressive relaxation*, Chicago 1928.

45. J. H. Schultz, *Das autogene Training*, Leipzig 1932.

46. M. Scheler, *Wesen und Formen der Sympathie*, Bonn 1923, p. 95 ff.

47. J. D. Hardy, 'Studies on pain', *Journal of clinical investigation* 19 (1940), pp. 659–680.

48. H. Piéron, loc. cit., note 26, p. 157.

49. Anything touching a peripheric nerve which has pain fibres causes pain, or anything touching the deep roots of the spinal cord. On the

other hand the tractus anterolateralis in the spinal cord itself, in which the pain fibres run to the brain, can be severed without an anaesthetic. 'It is an extraordinary fact but it is true,' says Leriche, q.v. p. 72; and further: 'Similarly the sensitive zone of the brain is usually painless and the brain can be cut, pressed, or cauterized without the least sensation being felt. Why, we do not know. Perhaps it is because we have not asked ourselves. Undoubtedly the brain is not apt to register and transmit a direct stimulation.'

50. H. W. Stenvers, 'Centrale pijn', *Psych. Neur. bladen* 41 (1937), p. 824.

51. J. D. Hardy, H. G. Wolff and H. Goodell, *Journ. of clinical investigation* 19 (1940), pp. 649, 659.

52. We are constantly being reminded of the fact that people bore pain much better in the past. Major operations, we are told, were performed without narcotics. The famous surgeon in Napoleon's army, Larrey, amputated legs and arms in the field and the wounded men simply sat and watched. In his memoirs he tells of an officer whose arm was amputated at the shoulder joint. He mounted his horse with the bandage on and took part in the normal cavalry expeditions right across Europe. Finally he arrived back in Paris, fully well. Leriche comments (p. 68) that a similar operation and behaviour after it are simply unthinkable in our own day. According to him, the difference does not lie in a difference of 'moral energy', but in our having got used to methods of easing pain. 'Like aspirin, surgical anaesthetics have made man more prone to suffer, because they have suppressed the pain of the operation and therefore prevented him from getting used to certain kinds of suffering.' This explanation is, however, oversimplified.

53. J. P. Pavlov, *Leçons sur l'activité du cortex cérébral*, Paris 1929. For criticism of Pavlov's theories, cf. Buytendijk and Plessner, 'Die physiologische Erklärung des Verhaltens. Eine Kritik an der Theorie Pawlows', *Acta Biotheoretica*, Series A, Vol. I, Part 3, Leyden 1935.

54. H. Rein, 'Zur Physiologie des Schmerzes', *Schmerz etc.* 12 (1939), pp. 129–39.

55. H. Higier, 'Der Schmerz als sympathische Erscheinung und seine Stellung zum animalen und vegetativen Nervensystem im allgemeinen', *Deutsche Zeitschr. f. Nervenheilk.* 89 (1926), pp. 196–210.

56. J. G. Dusser de Barenne, *Journ. de Psychol.* 28 (1931), p. 177.

57. R. Leriche, loc. cit., *Presse médicale*, 1931, p. 1.

58. F. A. Verbeek, 'De chirurgische behandeling der pijn', *Psychiatr. Neurol. bladen* 41 (1937), p. 179.
    V. von Weizsäcker, *Der Nervenarzt* 9 (1936), p. 553, is sceptical about sympathectomy in viceroalgia on the basis of Frazier (*Arch. of Neurol.* 19 (1928), p. 650), according to which of 13 cases operated on the sympathicus, one was cured—by Christian science!

59. Loc. cit., p. 895. This follows on the quotation in the text: 'characterized by a visible vasoconstriction as a result of a long vasokinetic reaction, introduced reflectorily by the trauma of the tissue'.

60. L. Davis and L. Pollock, 'The role of the autonomic nervous system in the production of pain', *Journ. of Amer. Med. Assoc.*, Vol. 106 (1936), p. 350.

61. L. J. Hut, *De sensibele chronaxie*, Diss. Groningen 1936 (Chapters V and VI). Cf. also Achelis, *Pflügers Arch.* 226 (1931), p. 212.
    Altenburger and Kroll, in *Deutsche Zeitschr. f. Nervenheilk.* 111 (1929), p. 144.
    E. T. von Brücke, *Ergebn. der Physiol.* 34 (1932), p. 220.

62. W. B. Cannon, *Bodily changes in pain, hunger, fear and rage*, New York 1920.

III. PAIN AND ANIMAL LIFE

63. R. Bilz, *Pars pro toto. Ein Beitrag zur Pathologie menschlicher Affekte und Organfunktionen*, Leipzig 1940, p. 100.

64. 'De rangorde der organismen in de biologie', *Tijdschr. voor Philosophie*, 3rd year, No. 1, 1941.

65. 'Das Verhalten des Oktopus nach teilweiser Zerstörung des *"Gehirns"* ', *Arch. Néerl. de Physiol. de l'homme et des animaux*, tome XVIII, le livraison (1933), p. 24.

66. *Wege zum Verständnis der Tiere*, Max Niehans Verlag, Zürich-Leipzig 1938.

67. The basic difference between action and expressive movement and the basis of an understanding of animal and human expression in Buytendijk and Plessner, 'Die Bedeutung des mimischen Ausdrucks', *Philos. Anzeiger*, Vol. I (1925).

68. *Grondproblemen van het dierlijk leven*, especially the chapter 'Het Instinkt', Antwerp 1938.
   Wesen und Sinn des Spiels, Berlin 1933.

69. A. P. Prince Auersperg, 'Schmerzproblem and vegetatives Nervensystem', *Wiener klin. Wochenschr.* 51 (1938), p. 106.

70. J. von Uexküll, *Theoretische Biologie*, Berlin 1928, p. 130.

71. M. Pradines, loc. cit., p. 121.

72. Leibniz, *Essais de Théodicée* III, p. 349.

73. Hedwig-Conrad Martius, *Ursprung und Aufbau des lebendigen Kosmos*, Otto Müller, Salzburg 1938.

74. 'Anschauliche Kennzeichen des Organischen', *Philos. Anzeiger.* II (1928), H.4.

75. Head and Rivers, 'A human experiment in nerve division', *Brain* 31 (1908), p. 428.

76. C. U. Ariëns Kappers, 'De anatomie en physiologie van den pijnzin', *Psych. en neurol. bladen* (1937), No. 6.
   Boeke en Heringa, *Verslagen Kon. Acad. von Wetensch.* 33 (1924).

77. Lewis and Pochin, 'Effects of Asphyxia and pressure on sensory nerves', *Journ. of clinical investigation* 3 (1937), p. 141.

78. G. E. Coghill, *Anatomy and the problem of human behaviour*, Cambridge 1929.

79. M. Scheler, *Vom Sinn des Leides*, Moralia, Leipzig 1923, p. 41.

80. J. von Uexküll, *Theoretische Biologie*, Berlin 1928, p. 130. The following is also very strange: 'Amoebas are able to differentiate pseudopodia of their own bodies from those belonging to others. It is not known how this is effected. They are in quite a different class from other animals. Since they have no structure which would be destroyed if they ate themselves, they are actually forced to swallow their own protoplasm constantly. Pain would query their whole existence.'

IV. PAIN AND EXPERIENCE

81. H. Bergson, *Matière et Mémoire*, Paris 1914, p. 44.

82. T. Elsenhans, *Lehrbuch der Psychologie*, 3rd edit. by F. Giese, revised by H. Greehle and F. Dorsch, Tübingen 1939, pp. 127–9 ('Die Haut als Schmerzvermittler').

83. F. Sauerbruch and H. Wenke, *Wesen und Bedeutung des Schmerzes*, Berlin 1936, p. 52 ff.

84. W. Wundt, *Physiologische Psychologie*, 3 vols., Leipzig 1908; C. Stumpf, *Gefühl und Gefühlsempfindung*, Leipzig 1928; cf. also 'Apologie der Gefühlsempfindungen', *Zeitschr. f. Psychol.* 75 (1916), p. 1.

O. Külpe, *Zur Psychologie der Gefühle*; Ber. ü. d. 6 Intern. Psychol. Kongress, Geneva 1909, pp. 183–96.

T. Ziehen, 'Eine Hypothese ü. d. sogenannten gefühlserzeugenden Prozess', *Zeitschr. f. Psychol.* (1903).

E. Becher, 'Gefühlsbegriff und Lust- und Unlustelemente', *Zeitschr. f. Psychol.* 74 (1916), p. 128.

85. F. Krüger, *Das Wesen der Gefühle*, Leipzig 1930 and *Die Tiefendimension und die Gegensätzlichkeit des Gefühlslebens*, Munich 1931.

86. M. F. Meyer, 'That whale among the fishes—the theory of the emotions', *Psychol. Review* 40 (1933), p. 292.

87. M. Scheler, *Der Formalismus in der Ethik und die materiale Wertethik*, Halle 1921, o.a. p. 345.

88. K. Schneider, *Zeitschr. f. Neurol.* 59 (1920), p. 281. *Pathopsychologie der Gefühle und Triebe*, Leipzig 1935.

89. E. Husserl, *Logische Untersuchungen*, Vol. 2, Halle, 2nd edit. (1913), pp. 393–5.

   'He [Brentano] differentiates, if not expressly, at any rate in meaning, between pain and pleasure sensations (sensations of feeling) and pain and pleasure in the sense of feelings. The content of the first, also the first to occur, is in his terminology "physical", and of the last "psychic phenomena", and therefore they belong to essentially different species. To me this conception appears completely true. . . .'

   'Pleasure and pain sensations can continue, even if the "Akt" characters based on them cease to exist.'

   J. P. Sartre (*L'Etre et le Néant*, N. R. F. 1943), differentiates between a pure simply experienced pain and the 'pain-object', the '*malum*' embraced by it.

   'The pure pain, since it is simply lived, cannot be grasped; it is one of those undefinable, undescribable things which simply are what they are' (398).

   Pure pain is also free from intentionality. It is an existence mode of consciousness itself, a manner in which consciousness exists in the body: 'the translucid matter of the consciousness, its *being-there*, its attachment to the world' (398). 'Objective pain, "*le mal*", has all the characteristics of pain, but it is transcendent and passive. "This pain is caressing, penetrating . . ." etc.' (401).

90. P. Natorp, *Allgemeine Psychologie* I, Tübingen 1912, p. 237.

91. E. Minkowski, *Vers une cosmologie*, F. Aubier, Paris 1936.

92. W. Stern, *Allgemeine Psychologie auf personalistischer Grundlage*, The Hague 1935.
   Gronart, 'Gefühl der Strebung', *Arch. ges. Psychol.* 79 (1931).

93. J. D. Achelis, *Pflügers Arch. f. Physiol.* 242 (1939), p. 644.

94. L. Klages, *Der Geist als Widersacher der Seele*, I, Vol. I, Leipzig 1937, o.a. p. 148. Also *Vom Wesen des Bewusstseins*, Leipzig 1933, and the work mentioned in note 20.

95. E. Straus, *Vom Sinn der Sinne*, Berlin 1935, p. 143.

96. W. Köhler, *Gestalt Psychology*, New York 1929, p. 96.

97. An objection may be made in that a person afflicted by pain does not utter a sound and that the same may be true of a person who is frightened. I do not know if diphthongs are the same among different peoples. In the case of animals, the production of sounds depends largely on the physical potentialities. Tradition and milieu have certainly a degree of influence on cries, exclamations, curses, etc., despite their so-called spontaneity. There are apparently no investigations on this subject. The explanation here given is only very tentative.

98. W. Preyer, *Die Seele des Kindes*, Leipzig 1890, p. 454. For criticism cf. Sauerbruch and Wenke, pp. 82-3.

99. C. Bühler, *Kindheit und Jugend*, Leipzig 1931, p. 182.

100. N. Hartmann, 'Zum Problem der Realitätsgegebenheit' (*Philos. Vorträge*, published by the Kantgesellschaft, No. 32), Berlin 1931, p. 17.

101. M. Scheler, *Die Stellung des Menschen im Kosmos*, Darmstadt 1928, p. 21.

102. Basler and Schuster, 'Über die Anpassung an die Empfindung von Hautschmerz', *Zeitschr. f. Biol.* 96 (1935), p. 333.

103. I. Kant, *Von der Macht des Gemüths durch den blossen Vorsatz seiner krankhaften Gefühle Meister zu sein*, Reklam-edit., p. 33.

104. H. Plessner, op. cit., note 21, p. 152.

105. M. Scheler, op. cit., note 87, p. 402.

106. R. von Ihering, *Der Kampf um's Recht*. Reklam-edit., cit. in Sauerbruch and Wenke, p. 68.

107. E. Straus, op. cit., note 15, p. 143.

108. J. von Kries, op. cit., note 36, p. 22.

109. W. H. von Wyss, *Körperlich-seelische Zusammenhänge in Gesundheit und Krankheit*, Leipzig 1931.
    Dunbar H. Flanders, *Emotions and Bodily Changes*, Columbia Univ. Press, New York 1935.

110. M. Picard, *Das Menschengesicht*, Munich 1929, p. 132.

111. M. Scheler, op. cit., note 79, p. 92.

112. F. Nietzsche, *Jenseits von Gut und Böse*, Kroner edit. Vol. 8, p. 258.

113. M. Scheler, 'Zur Rehabilitierung der Tugend', *Abhandlungen und Aufsätze*, Vol. I, Leipzig 1915, p. 17 ff.

114. C. J. Warden, *Animal motivation*, Univ. Press, New York-Columbia 1931.

115. M. Scheler, op. cit., note 79, p. 57.

116. G. Thibon, 'Propositions sur la douleur', *Etudes carmélitaines*, 20th year, Vol. II (1936), p. 142.

    Two works by H. Kranz, 'Über den Schmerz' (*Aufsätze und Reden der Senckenbergischen Naturforschenden Gesellschaft*, Frankfurt-a.-M., 1947), and 'Die Stellung des Schmerzes unter den Empfindungen' (Festschrift für Kurt Schneider, 1947), could not be taken into account.

V. ANNEX

117. Macmillan, New York 1942.

118. H. K. Beecher, 'The measurement of pain', *Pharmacological Review* 9 (1957), pp. 59–203.

119. A. E. McKenna, 'The experimental approach to pain', *Journ. of Applied Physiol.* 13 (1958), pp. 449–56.

120. H. G. Wolff and S. Wolf, *Pain*, Blackwell Scientific Publications, Oxford 1958, p. 5.

    H. G. Wolff and J. D. Hardy, 'On the nature of pain', *Physiol. Review* 27 (1947), pp. 167–98.

121. Wolff and Wolf, p. 19.

122. 'Über den Schmerz', *Psyche* 9 (1956), pp. 436–52.

123. K. Hansen, Die diagnostische Bedeutung des Schmerzes', *Acta Neurovegetativa* VII (1955), pp. 301–27.

124. A. von Auersperg, 'Die Schmerzempfindung von prädilektivem Typus', *Der Nervenarzt* 22 (1951), pp. 22–6.

125. J. A. Capps, *An experimental and clinical study of pain in the pleura, pericardium and peritoneum*, New York 1932.

126. H. G. Wolff and J. D. Hardy, op. cit. (1947), p. 194.

127. J. Cohen, *Humanistic Psychology*, London 1958, p. 86.

128. J. C. White and W. H. Sweet, *Pain. Its mechanisms and neurosurgical control*, Springfield, U.S.A. 1955.

129. Leriche, 'Qu'est-ce que la douleur?' in *La douleur et les douleurs*, publ. by Th. Alajouanine, Paris, Masson 1957, p. 6.

130. D. O. Hebb, *Organization of behaviour*, New York 1949, p. 186.

131. W. Noordenbos, *Pain: problems pertaining to the transmission of nerve impulses which give rise to pain*, Elsevier publ. Comp., Amsterdam-London-New York-Princeton 1959, p. 173.

132. T. Cohen, op. cit., p. 91.

133. D. O. Hebb, op. cit., p. 185.

134. W. Noordenbos, op. cit., p. 108.

135. W. Noordenbos, op. cit., p. 176.

136. A. von Auersperg, Orlando Aidar, Erhart A. Erzos, 'Disturbances of sensation occasioned by experimental arrest of bloodflow', *Arquivos de Neuro-Psiquiatria* (1949), Vol. III, pp. 371–392.

137. Kornetsky, *Journ. comp. physiol. psychol.* 47 (1954), pp. 130–2. (Quoted by Beecher, op. cit., p. 183.)

138. A. Mitscherlich and G. Ruffler, 'Der Schmerz als Symbol', *Mediz. Klinik* 51 (1956), pp. 909–13.

139. Th. S. Szasz, *Pain and Pleasure. A study of bodily feelings*, London 1957.

140. L. Michaux, 'Les aspects psychiatriques de la douleur somatique' in *La douleur et les douleurs*, Paris 1957, pp. 267–88.

141. F. Curtius, 'Psyche und Schmerz', *Mediz. Klinik* 50 (1955), pp. 1691–5.

142. H. Bürger-Prinz, 'Zur Psychologie des Schmerzes', *Nervenarzt* 22 (1951), p. 376.

143. H. K. Beecher, op. cit., p. 169.

144. H. Hécaen, 'L'asymbolie a la douleur' in *La douleur et les douleurs*, Paris 1957, pp. 259–65.

145. See also E. C. O. Jensbury, 'Insensitivity to pain', *Brain* 74 (1951), pp. 336–53.

146. H. G. Wolff and J. D. Hardy, op. cit., (1947), p. 193.

Index